Jorge's

Rx

Questions and Answers
as previously published in
High Times Magazine
by

Jorge
Cervantes

CREDITS

Copyright 2003 by Jorge Cervantes

Written by Jorge Cervantes

Edited by E. Cervantes, Skip Stone

Book designed by Martin Trip

Illustrations by E. Cervantes, M. Trip

Photographs by Jorge Cervantes, unless otherwise noted.

Cover photo by Goyo, leaf drawn by Cody K. Wombold

ISBN: 1-878823-30-2

Printed in the United States of America

Visit Jorge's website www.marijuanagrowing.com for a glossary of terms in this book and others from Senor Cervantes. Also on the site is more growing information, the latest techniques and tips; and how to order other books from Jorge Cervantes.

Wholesale Distribution in North America by:
Homestead Book Co., Tel. 1-800-426-6777
Quick Distribution, Tel. 1-510-527-7036
Retail sales in North America are via:
FS Book Company, Tel. 1-800-635-8883

DEDICATION

This book is dedicated to the memory of
Tammy Faye (Fifi) Cervantes.
Thanks to Fifi for being such a fine companion and wonderful guard.

TABLE OF CONTENTS

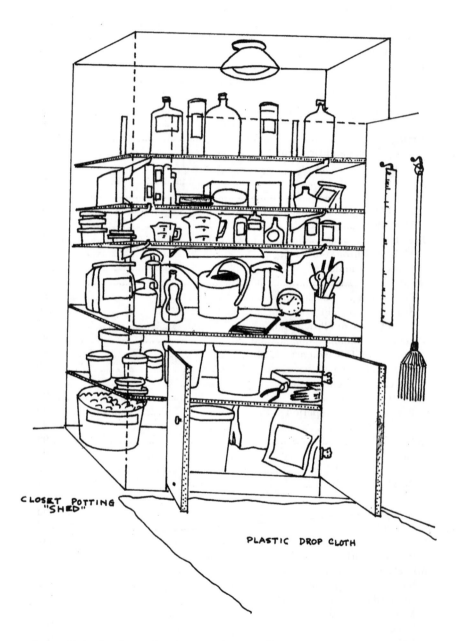

CLOSET POTTING
"SHED"

PLASTIC DROP CLOTH

A closet is perfect for storing your growing supplies.

FIRST TIME GROWER

FIRST TIME

Dear Jorge,

I am growing for the first time. I read all of your columns, but I have no first-hand experience. What is a good light cycle for vegging my plants? What kind of fertilizer should I use and when? How do I clone? Can you recommend anything that would help?

Thanx,

The Jungleman, Newark, NJ

Dear Jungleman,

Use the KISS method, Keep It Simple Stoner. Concentrate on the basics: light, water/nutrients, air, temperature, and growing medium (soil). Your best bet is to read a book and follow the instructions. Check out *Marijuana Indoors: Five Easy Gardens*. It has all the information you need to grow in the first case study of a closet garden.

Start seedlings under 16-18 hours of fluorescent light. Give clones 18-24 hours of light. Grow vegetative plants under 18 hours of HID light. Use a high quality water soluble hydroponic fertilizer. Clone mother plants by cutting off a 2-4-inch branch from the mother plant. Trim the bottom leaves and shoots from the stem, leaving the bottom half of the stem bare. Dip the cut end in a rooting gel. Insert the cut end in a pre-made hole in a rooting medium and water until saturated. Place clones under 24 hours of fluorescent light.

Beginners often get sidetracked and concentrate on the wrong things. That's why the basics are so important! Remember to keep the ambient temperature in the clone room no higher than 80 degrees, preferably about 70. Keep the growing medium a little warmer, about 75 degrees F., than the air temperature. This will hasten root growth. They have no roots at first and need to be misted to compensate. Learning how to water is crucial. Transplant after you can see plenty of roots growing out of the growing medium. Don't be afraid to take a few extra clones to experiment. If some die, you need replacements.

About the fourth week after clones are moved, novice growers often see signs of nutrient deficiencies/excesses manifested in sickly growth and discolored leaves. The problem has been around for several weeks, only now it is evident in leaves. Circumvent this problem by giving plants the proper fertilizer regimen. Read and follow fertilizer instructions. Always water 20-30 percent more than necessary and let the excess drain out the bottom of the pot. Every 30 days, leach pots with 2-3 times as much water as the volume of growing medium. This will wash away most nutrient problems.

ROOKIE ON A TRIP

  Hello Jorge

I have an area 38 x 62 x 84 inches, I would like try growing. I want to use a 600w light with a wick hydroponic system, because I'm out of town a lot. I am a complete rookie at this, so I need to know the whole nine yards!

Also can you recommend any books for this kind of system? I read HIGH TIMES, but a lot of it is over my head.

Keep up the good work, and thanks,

Internet.com

Dear Internet.com,

You are asking me to give you advice on how to make one of the most common mistakes growers make – not pay attention to your garden and expect it to yield beaucoup bud because it is a low maintenance hydroponic (wick) system. Regardless of what you read and what advertisers tell you, a wick hydroponic system is not a substitute for a few minutes per day spent maintaining your garden. Remember, their goal is to sell hydroponic systems, not grow plants. First, you need experience growing several crops to develop the knowledge you lack. Once you have a feel for growing, you can experiment with leaving the system alone for a few days and see what happens.

If you want to start a garden, then leave it for a few days; expect a few problems. The first problem you will encounter is a lack of water. This problem may be able to be solved with a wick system that uses a wick to transfer water from a reservoir via a wick to the growing medium. But you must have a very pure water supply that is not contaminated with dissolved solids or too hard, containing a lot of calcium.

The wick hydroponic system may solve only the watering problem. It does not solve possible ventilation, heat, insect, fungus, nutrient or lighting problems. These challenges can be met only with a vigilant eye and experience.

As for books that will explain the "whole nine yards", I suggest *Marijuana Indoors: Five Easy Gardens & Indoor Marijuana Horticulture - The Indoor Bible* by Jorge Cervantes, also *Hydroponic Gardening* by Steven Carthorse.

MY FIRST GARDEN,

Q Dear Jorge,

This is my first garden I have been able to flower. I have one male and a female that have been flowering for three weeks and two females flowering for one week. The first female is showing small flower clusters with white pistols. I have started using an organic blooming tea, which seems to be working well. They have slowed down after the white pistols grew. When and what can I do to help them fill out and tighten up? I am using a 270w Son Agro. How long does this process take?

Islo, Southern California

A Dear Islo,

Waiting is difficult. Expect a harvest from 8 – 12 weeks after turning the lights to 12-hour days. Buds often mature a few days later when using a smaller HID. Flowering is fast at first, stems elongate and pistils appear after about two weeks. Growth slows about the fourth week. Light intensity is the most important factor in your garden. Make sure the light is close enough – 12 – 18 inches – to plants so they receive intense light. Turn plants every day so they get light on both sides.

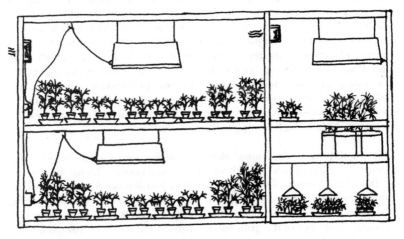

Two flowering rooms are supplied with clones grown in two small clone/vegetative rooms.

SMALL SPACE GROW SHOWS

SMALL SPACE

Jorge,

I'm going to grow hydro with a 250w metal halide, and eight 20w fluorescent grow bulbs in a fairly small space. Is this a good setup? I plan to harvest small clones. What kind of fertilizer should I use in the sandy growing medium? I only have access to mainstream home and garden stores, K-Mart, Wal-Mart, etc. Does cigarette ash contain a substantial amount of nitrogen?

Soon to be smokin' free
With a little help from my friends, VA

Dear Smokin' Free,

A 250-watt metal halide generates up to 23,000 lumens with a lumen-per-watt conversion of 92. A 1000w metal halide generates 115,000 lumens with a lumen-per-watt of 115. A 250-watt bulb can cover a 2.5 x 3-foot flowering area. The 250w bulb uses 3-kilowatt hours of electricity every 12-hour day. At $0.10 per KWH, that's only $0.30 a day extra power. Eight 20w fluorescent bulbs (20 x 8 = 160) uses 160 watts with 23 lumens-per-watt, to generate 3,680 lumens. The fluorescent light not only delivers considerably fewer lumens per watt of electricity consumed, the lumens fade very fast. This bright/dim incongruence is most apparent when you want to grow vegetative plants under the fluorescent and move them under the halide to flower. Chances are the plants under the fluorescents will grow at a much slower rate than those under the halide. To avoid problems with timing, allow plants enough time to grow under the fluorescent lights. Take two or three times as many clones as you need. Thin the clones down to 6 or eight healthy plants to move into the flowering room.

Use any all purpose "complete" water-soluble fertilizer such as Miracle Gro or Peters during vegetative growth and a "blossom booster" blend for flowering. Take special care to fertilize lightly. It's easy to overdo. Also make sure to flush growing containers with plenty of water once a month. Nutrient buildup in containers is one of the main problems most growers face. Keep cigarette ashes and smoke out of the grow room environment. Tobacco ash has a pH of about 10 and contains very little nourishment for plants. Any of the good stuff, such as ammonia (a form of nitrogen), which puts nicotine into a "free base" for faster absorption into the blood stream, is volatized into the air. Make sure to have a good vent fan that will change the air in the room every few minutes. Also buy a basic grow guide, such as *Pot for Pennies* or *Marijuana Indoors: Five Easy Gardens*.

If you keep this small grow room running properly, you should be able to harvest about 0.3 to 0.4 grams per watt per month. 0.3 grams x 250 watts = 75 grams (2.6 ounces) or 0.4 x 250 = 100 grams (3.5 ounces). Smaller halide bulbs have a lower lumen-per-watt conversion and yield less dope, but that's OK!

CLOSET CULTIVATOR

Dear Jorge:

I am an indoor grower with very little experience. I am moving and want to start fresh at my new apartment where I have limited space and equipment. I am planning on using a closet 7 x 4 x 3 feet and one 400w HPS bulb. Do you have any advice for growing in this small area? Are there certain growing methods that work well in small spaces? Also, are there any particular strains that will grow well in this environment?

Thanks,

Ross, New York City

Dear Ross,

The closet should allow you plenty of room to set up two grow rooms, a mother/clone room below and a flowering room above. Plan and set up the entire grow room before introducing plants. The bottom clone/mother room can be illuminated with four to eight 20w fluorescent bulbs and take up the bottom three feet of the closet. The top part of the garden is reserved for flowering. There is an excellent case study of a similar garden in *Marijuana Indoors: Five Easy Gardens*, by Jorge Cervantes and other great examples in *Closet Cultivator*, by Ed Rosenthal; both books are available through HIGH TIMES bookstore.

Growing plants in a flood and drain bed using 4-inch rockwool cubes or small one-gallon containers allow small plants to be packed very closely together. If you add one or two clones every few days to the flowering garden, you can also harvest one or two plants every few days.

Jorge's Rx:
Super Size Secret: Keep the temperature of the rooting medium at 78-80 degrees and ambient air temperature 6-8 degrees cooler than the rooting medium, day and night. Root growth increases dramatically.

GROW CUBE

Jorge,

After reading the article "Grow Cube" (J.P. Jarvis, Aug '01 HT), I started thinking about starting a simple and small growing chamber. The article says the cube is ideal for cloning but touches only briefly on its flexibility for flowering. Can you use the Grow Cube for one plant from seedling to harvest?

Is the high pressure sodium bulb a must, or will one of the fluorescent "twisty" bulbs do the trick in combination with the four fluorescent strips? What other details should I take into account before trying to grow in such a limited space?

Newbie, Trenton, NJ

Dear Newbie,

The Grow Cube works great to grow seedlings or clones until they are a foot tall, but when it comes to flowering, light is lacking. The 15 x 15 x 48-inch box has four 15w fluorescents for a total of 60 watts. To provide enough light for a fair crop of sinsemilla, the box would have to be packed with eight 15w fluorescent tubes – total 120w. But, that would create a heat problem within the Grow Cube that would require a fan to dissipate. I have seen fair buds mature under fluorescents. Remember that light diminishes (exponentially) to the square of the distance.

The closet without walls above shows how twelve containers easily fit on a 3 x 4-foot hydroponic table.

This means that light fades super fast. Flowering plants require more intense light than seedlings, clones or vegetative plants. Save time and invest in a HID lamp that will supply enough light.

SECURITY

HEAT-SEEKING VOYEURS ILLEGAL!

Dear Jorge,

Can the cops use high tech electronics to see into my house and look for marijuana gardens?

Heat Sensitive, Detroit, MI

Dear Heat Sensitive,

No! No! No! Cops can't use thermal imaging devices to secure a search warrant. On June 11, 2001 the Supreme Court rendered a split, 5-4, decision that ruled use of thermal imaging or other technology to measure heat patterns of exterior surfaces of dwellings and other buildings without first securing a search warrant is a violation of the Constitution. Thermal imaging technology was used, almost without exception, to secure search warrants.

But be weary! Cops can still legally toss your trash around, fly over your backyard looking for incriminating evidence and lie to you legally.

MAIL ORDER SECURITY

I want to order a book from www.amazon.com but I am afraid the DEA will use the information to kick down my door and haul me away! Am I too paranoid?

Bud Book, Cyberspace

Dear Bud,

I called the legal and customer service departments at amazon.com. I asked them questions for about 20 minutes. To date the DEA has not subpoenaed records from patrons that bought cultivation books. They hammered over and over that their privacy policy is intact and assured me they do not give any information to anybody for any reason. However, I have heard several stories about local authorities and the DEA getting a hold of UPS shipping records, telephone and electric records of growers. In all of the stories these records were willingly handed over by the agencies involved. Any grower that orders merchandise via UPS, RPS or courier service should not have the merchandise shipped to the locale where the grow show is located. Making telephone calls from a grow house to order products or seek information from hydroponic stores or bookstores is also taboo. Credit card purchases should be routed via a third party and not belong to the grower.

Patrons that mail order merchandise should do so with a money order to
avoid a trail to their front door! For more information buy the book *How to
Use Mail Drops*, $16.95 from FS Books 1-800-635-8883, www.fsbookco.com.

SECURITY CHECKLIST:

 Electric bill should be about the same as the neighbors and previous tenants

 Garden and grounds should be tidy and similar to neighbors

 No light leaks whatsoever

 Use friend's car to visit grow store

 No noise – humming, fan on/off at night, etc.

 No strange odors including ozone smell

SHIPPING SEEDS

 Greetings Jorge,

In recent HIGH TIMES you wrote about growing after 9/11. Do you think
ordering seeds via snail mail nowadays would be unwise? I'd like to but I'm
paranoid.

 V. Rette, Ontario, California

Dear V.,

You have every right to be paranoid. Americans are taught to be paranoid. I
recently spoke to numerous seed merchants that ship worldwide, none of
which had any problems sending seeds to other countries. Some seed companies do not send seeds to countries where seeds are prohibited by law. For up-
to-date information about seed companies, hit Green Man's site,
http://www.seedbankupdate.com. This site is updated every week.

TOP 13 WAYS GROW ROOMS ARE DISCOVERED

1. Snitch turns you in
2. Burglary
3. Fire
4. Odors leak outside
5. Water leaks outside house/apartment/room
6. Weird trash – soil, grow stuff and supplies
7. Fan noise
8. Suspicious traffic at odd hours
9. Dreadlocks, hippy clothing
10. Loose lips and business practices
11. Outdoor crops near grow room
12. Carrying too much stuff in and out
13. Loud parties

SECURITY IS TOPS!

Dear Jorge,

Please print my list of how grow rooms are discovered it is very important.

Peace & love,

Baba Otis

Dear Baba,

Thanks for caring so much about your fellow growers. Your list is very important! According to other growers, you may want to include an excessively high electric bill, frequenting other grow rooms, being outspoken and politically active in legalization movements, pissing off cops and ordering grow merchandise via UPS that is sent to the grow location to your list.

SECURE ENOUGH?

Dear Jorge,

I have decided to start growing in my apartment. Security is my biggest concern. I plan to grow in my closet in a small hydro setup with a 400w light and start clones with fluorescents. I do not want my neighbors to know, so I bought an ionizer to stop the smell.

Paranoid in Alabama

Dear Paranoid,

You have good reason to feel the way you do. Americans that live in the USA enjoy fewer freedoms than residents from any other industrialized country in the world. The proof is in the number of annual arrests for marijuana consumption, cultivation and dealing. Last year drug arrests topped 750,000! In 2000 one out of every 373 people in the US was arrested for a drug-related offense. Today one out of every 150 people is incarcerated. Neighbors and family members are encouraged to turn users into the authorities. The police do not care if the information comes from a disgruntled mate, co-worker, parent, sister, brother or competitor. Often, the informant is not required to be identified. Today, racketeering laws that were enacted to jail organized mafia members are used against honest peace-loving citizens.

Bust-happy police often stretch the rules to rid society of pot growers and tokers. Remember it is legal for authorities to use deception (they can lie to you) and often regard nothing you own or owned as sacred. We can anticipate the new laws that are aimed at catching terrorists (actual bad guys) will be used against honest citizens for other crimes against society, just the way the RICO laws were turned against them.

Here are a few things that smart growers do. The list below is just a start and is as important as not talking to anybody personally or via telephone about toking, growing and dealing in the USA or keeping the beautiful bouquet of buds from passersby.

Never leave a paper trail that leads to you. Do not order grow equipment with your credit card and have it shipped to the address where growing is taking place. Always send a money order and have the equipment sent to a "safe" address.

Send e-mails via a "safe" connection that cannot be traced back to you. Once e-mail has been sent or received, delete all traces of it on the computer.

Never throw away grow related garbage, including soil, rockwool, information, stems or seeds in your garbage can. Police can legally check your garbage for "evidence" to obtain a search warrant.

Do not go to a "grow store" in your own vehicle.

Do not trade clones or seeds with anybody in the "land of the free."

STEALING POT!

High Jorge!

I just picked up October's issue and read where some dude tried stealing plants, telling you he "found" them. I appreciate your response to him. My plants were just stolen the week before! Oh man, I worked so hard, since I planted them on April 20 (4-20). The beautiful Columbian Gold hybrids were about 3 weeks from harvest. They broke in and stole plants! Keep it peaceful!

Lil Dead Flower Child, Tucson, AZ

Dear Lil Dead,

My condolences. Apparently the theft story touched a nerve. I received numerous responses to that letter. I am still disheartened by the lack of respect thieves, law enforcement and much of society has when it comes to the sacred herb. Our society is lopsided when we cannot count on the police to protect our assets. I believe Swiss activist, Bernard Rapaz, said it best: "An unguarded marijuana field is like a bank without walls." One day the craziness will stop and the jackals will feed on each other instead the fruits, labors and dreams of honest descent citizens.

NARC LANDLADY

Dear Jorge,

Please tell readers about this trick by the cops and apartment managers. If we band together, we can keep more human beings out of America's hellholes! My 50 year old apartment manager appears nice and intelligent. She even hinted that she smoked pot in the 60s. She told me many times that she is required by local law to participate in a program that teaches her how to find marijuana growers. One day I caught her recording electrical usage with a pencil and paper on the meters behind the building. She looked as guilty as the cat that just ate the canary when I asked her what she was doing.

It gets worse. Three days after receiving my electric bill, I received a "knock and talk" from the plain-clothes apartment surveillance officer. Now alerted to living in a police state, I looked through the security hole in the door. I did not open the door. He left his business card, and I called him so I did not arouse more suspicion. I believe he lied to me when he said he was investigating the person that used to live in my apartment. Cops are tricky bastards that lie to get what they want.

Jorge, you told an apartment dweller to use a 400w HID in a past column. Well, I used to use one, and it used a suspicious amount of electricity. Now I use a 250w lamp and I think all is cool.

Me, Phoenix, AZ

Dear Me,

Phoenix has always been a hotbed of DEA activity. A program to ferret out peaceful gardeners sponsored by the cops is definitely an element of a police state. Thank you for sharing this information with readers. Have you moved yet?

PURCHASE PARANOIA

Jorge,

I live in California and was talking to someone and they told me that if I went to a grow shop to buy a 1000 watt light set up that they will ask for a drivers license number to buy it even if you pay cash so the local authorities can follow up on it? Is this bullshit?

MotoX

Dear MotoX,

Bullshit. However, legitimate garden centers have been the target of numerous investigations. Growers that want to be safe take normal precautions: only call such stores from a pay phone, never go to the store in a car registered to a grower or parked at a grow show, pay all bills in cash, and most importantly, never mention they are doing anything illegal to anybody.

HID lights and growing supplies are also available from Home Depot and other home improvement centers, often at discount prices.

BIG BROTHER!

Jorge,

I want to grow for personal consumption but even with a small hydroponic setup up for 7 plants I will need a 1000w lamp. How on earth do you mask the increase in power consumption from big brother?

Paranoid, Harrisburg, PA

Dear Paranoid,

Who says you have to use a 1000w lamp? You can easily use a 400w bulb and grow all the dope you want in an area up to four feet square. Lower electric consumption by turning down your water heater thermostat from 170 to 130 degrees F. and minimize use of electrical appliances in your home.

MEDICAL MARIJUANA

CURED MY ACNE!

Jorge,

Did you know that cannabis changed my life? It healed my chronic acne. I am 33 years old. After years of treatment I discovered that cannabis flowers have a powerful healing effect on my skin disease. I smoke 'White Shark' from the Greenhouse Seed Co. The plant helps my metabolism to control the sebum production of my skin. Now I can have a better life. My face, neck and chest are totally recovered from those horrible and painful spots. I use one gram two or three times a week. I want to share this information with other people that suffer from this disease. It works for me and I am very happy now! I wish you a long life.

Sincerely,

Mathias Farnallier, Amsterdam, Zuidoost, Netherlands

Dear Mathias,

Thank you for sharing this important information with HIGH TIMES readers. I sincerely hope that this cure works on others too. Your story is very inspiring and proves that more medical research on cannabis is necessary. Spineless politicians and government officials are keeping medicinal cannabis from needy patients. Their personal agenda and inbred fear only promote more ignorance and fear. The Netherlands recently legalized cannabis for medicinal use, and for good reason, it is effective medicine for a growing number of ailments!

Jorge's Prescription:

Use the power of the internet, even if you don't have it at home, most public libraries have internet access.
Check websites such as www.cannabishealth.com for more information that is not dictated by the US Government as propaganda. Alternative publications are more likely to tell the truth than large commercially and politically controlled media outlets.

SUPPOSITORIES

Help me Jorge,

Now that my state has passed legal medicinal marijuana I am ready to begin growing my own, but I have a problem. Smoking it makes me cough so much that I get sicker than before. The THC calms me to function and sleep. I like the effect, I just don't like eating it, because it takes too long to act and I can't smoke it. I'm not sure what to do. How can I get a faster reaction to the THC without smoking it?

Puking Potaholic

Dear PP,

Suppositories. I recently made friends with two Swiss nationals that have invented cannabis suppositories. Suppositories are an excellent way to ingest cannabis quickly without suffering the side effects caused by inhaling smoke. Below is a copy of a recipe to make suppositories.

I have experimented with the suppositories made from this recipe and can vouch they work and work well. The effect kicks you in the ass in 10 to 15 minutes. The effect is a bit different than smoking, more of a body stone than a head rush.

The recipe is simple and maybe you would like to try it out.

You will need:

Cacao butter (97 percent), beeswax (3 percent) and screened resin (hash) from buds.
The dosage is approximately 300 milligrams per "serving" for what we call the "medium screen."

Melt the cacao butter in a small container. Heat water in a large pan and place a small glass containing the cacao butter in the hot water. The cacao butter melts at just over 100 degrees F. When melted add the beeswax. It will melt also. Be careful not to exceed the temperature, 120 degrees F. If exceeded it will alter the properties of cacao butter and you will have to throw it out. It's better to proceed slowly and take your time to avoid overheating the mix. Once all is melted add the cannabis resin powder and stir occasionally. Keep the solution cooking at the low temperature (between 100 and 110 degrees for 15 minutes. Carefully fill small gelatin capsules with the mix and let cool slowly at room temperature (70 degrees F). Do not cool them rapidly. Cooling slowly lets the ingredients crystallize slowly and evenly. Let them sit for a day or two. Store in a cool dry place, such as the refrigerator.

Insert the suppository as you would any other. Once inserted, wait for about 30 minutes to make sure the complete effect has manifested before inserting another. Be careful, these things can knock you on your ass!

THIEVES!!!

Dear Jorge,

I was reading in October's issue of HIGH TIMES about the thief that overheard some "friends" talking about a patch of marijuana they "found"! It was probably mine!! My husband is quadriplegic and smokes pot for the medical benefit, which eases his pain. The thing that really makes me angry is that thieves, damn them, can't grow their own so they have to steal it from someone who really needs it! I grew three plants in my backyard; they were just starting to bud, when some jerk(s) stole them, even before they were ready. The crooks were thoughtless enough to leave the smallest plant hanging on the fence! I'm venting because it makes me mad they have to steal from someone who can't go and plant in a field because it is not wheelchair accessible! They will not get my plants again, they will be monitored 24/7!

Thanks for letting me vent!!

Lisa, Via Internet

Dear Lisa,

Your story is sad and compelling. I sincerely hope that would-be thieves read it carefully and look deep within themselves before stealing from one who needs medicine that is unobtainable legally in your state. Remember that law enforcement also plays the same role as low-life scum-sucking thieves when it comes to medical marijuana in most states. The only reason they are able to deprive ailing US citizens of their medicine is because the society lets them. We are the society and we must mandate the change!

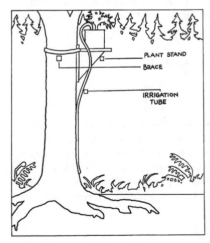

A couple of suggestions for hiding your outdoor crops.

ARTHRITIS

Dear Jorge,

I have horrible arthritis from head to toe and cannot take any more non-steroid pills because they cause bleeding. I cannot take narcotics because they give me insomnia. I am not interested in taking any of the cancer drugs such as Enbrel and Remicade (IMO), which are too dangerous. They can cause infections and too many people have already died from them.

Is there any type/brand/species of marijuana that would knock the pain down?

Is there any kind that would help with the pain, yet NOT make the brain fuzzy/high? I'd like to be able to wash the windows and yard work, etc; but without being high, or at least not too high.

I have no intention of driving the car. Am I expecting to find a marijuana that does not exist?

Thanks

Mary Ann, Internet

Dear Mary Ann,

Living with arthritis must be very difficult indeed, especially when official pain relief is limited to non-existent. In general, marijuana lowers the pressure in the body, mellows you out and relieves pain. In general indica varieties are more sedative while sativas are more uplifting. Both get you high. Scientists recently discovered a substance that appears to block cannabinoid receptors in the brain, which nullifies the high while allowing all the other physical effects. Unfortunately, this is in the research stage now and could take years before it is available to the public.

SUFFERING SINGLE MOTHER

Dear Jorge,

Smoking has made life bearable after disk surgery on my back four years ago. I am a single mother and need to keep my expenses low. I started eight plants under two fluorescent tubes in the closet two weeks ago. They are in a medium sized clay pot under 24 hours of light. Do I keep adding bulbs as they get bigger? All the lights you talk about in HIGH TIMES sound complicated and pricey. How do I know when they are ready to flower? Please help me stay happy and sane!

Love,

Mom, Ctown, WV

Dear Mom,

Back pain can be unbearable. Fortunately marijuana helps ease your pain. You can keep adding fluorescent tubes, as plants get bigger. Growing under fluorescents will net you a bit of bud, but much less than under a small HID. A two-tube 80w fluorescent setup costs about $25. A 100w metal halide costs about $150, a 175w $200 and a 250w $225 including postage via mail order. The initial cost of each fluorescent watt is about $0.31 per watt ($25 divided by 80) and metal halides are 100w = $1.50 per watt, 175w = $1.15 per watt, and the initial cost of a 250w = $0.90 per watt. Your best value is to buy a 250w metal halide. The lights are very simple to deploy, you hang the lamp from the ceiling, plug it into a timer and plug the timer into the electrical outlet. Just the same as you would with a fluorescent setup. A 250w metal halide will net three times the yield as the same number of fluorescent watts. Granted the initial cost is more, but when you weigh this sum against net yield the decision is easy. I also suggest a simple easy book for you, *Marijuana Indoors: Five Easy Gardens*, $14.95, available from HIGH TIMES bookstore.

This White Widow plant was grown out-doors on a south-facing balcony in Amsterdam one fine summer. This photo was taken at four weeks of flowering, and the plant was harvested after 10 weeks of flowering. Completely organic, this plant yeilded enough to keep a medical patient happy for two months.

Outdoor Growing

Moving Outdoors

  Dear Jorge,

My friend grows and he said if I wanted a clone I could grow it outside. But the plant is not used to heavy ultraviolet rays from the sun. It will burn the shit out of it. How can I move the clone outdoors and not beat the shit burned out of it?

Wee Willie Reefer
Seattle, WA

  Dear Wee Willie,

It's only March and you are ready to put plants outdoors? You could be a couple of months early. The biggest problems you will have are low temperatures, wind and rain. Few people will suspect marijuana plants in a greenhouse this time of year. Ultraviolet light is only a concern if you are high in the mountains or under the ozone hole in Australia. This time of the year in the Pacific Northwest should still be cool enough to expect a killing freeze, so plants will need to be protected from the weather until mid-April.

Plant clones in an unheated greenhouse if temperatures do not dip below 25 degrees F. Heat the greenhouse if the temperature drops down to 20 degrees. Usually an incandescent light bulb is all that's necessary for heat.

Move the plants out into the greenhouse for an hour during the first day. Increase the time by one hour daily for 7–14 days. The plants should be "hardened-off" by the end of the last day and be able to spend nights in the greenhouse.

Outside In?

Jorge,

I have a plant outdoors. I was wondering if I could bring it inside and put it under a HPS. Will this kill my plant?

Thank you,

Matt, Cyberspace

Shelving and spacing account for much additional grow room space. Remember, plants grow wherever the light shines.

Dear Matt,

Bringing outdoor plants indoors makes sense. Since harvest season is upon us, you might first consider harvesting the plants. If they are not too big, you can dig them up, put them in pots and bring them inside. Even though you may sever some roots, plants will probably live if you line the pot with commercial potting soil and give them plenty of water.

Give the transplants at least 18 hours of light for 6 to 8 weeks, until strong vegetative growth appears. Flip the lights to a 12/12 on/off schedule to induce flowering. You will have a new crop by the end of January. Do not use the plants as "mothers" because re-flowering can cause a slight decline in potency.

HOMEMADE GREENHOUSE?

Dear Jorge,

I live in beautiful British Columbia Canada and I want to build a greenhouse in the wilderness and grow weed inside. I plan to cover the outside and inside of the frame structure with heavy plastic. I will catch irrigation water that condenses from the walls in a bucket. There will be minimal air circulation in the 5 x 8 x 6-foot greenhouse. I'm still in the planning stages and I would like to know if this is a good plan.

Thanks very much.

Me:), from BC

Dear MBC,

Greenhouses in the wilderness stick out like a sore thumb and get ripped off! If you are going to grow outdoors, grow under the natural sunshine and camouflage the garden and protect it from the deer. If you can place the greenhouse inside your back yard or next to the house, you will have a lot better luck harvesting a crop. Covering the inside and outside of the frame with plastic means you can fill the chamber between the two sheets of plastic with air. This layer of air will insulate the greenhouse, obscure light and peering eyes. Simply set up a 140 CFM blower to fill the chamber between the two sheets of plastic. The insulation will diminish condensation substantially. Water that condenses on the walls means the humidity is 100 percent! Not a good thing. You will need to vent the greenhouse to keep the temperature below 85 degrees F and the humidity below 60 percent. If the humidity and temperature go unchecked, you have just opened the door to insect, spider mite and disease. The space you have is small (40-square feet), but with the proper management, you can easily harvest a couple of pounds every summer.

CHANGING CLIMATES

Hola Jorge,

I recently moved from Ft. Worth, Texas to Dayton, Ohio. I would like to talk to local farmers to find out about the climate, soil and water. How would I do this without sounding like a narc? The soil here compared to Texas is a lot better!

Got your books...keep up the great work!

Calyx, Dayton, OH

Dear Calyx,

You are smart to consult with experts before investing a lot of time making mistakes. I once knew a greenhouse grower that moved from Texas to Seattle, WA. He was an expert grower in Texas, but did not know the maritime Northwest climate. He made a few simple mistakes one year while growing poinsettias and soon went bankrupt.

Look in your local phone book under "County Government." Look for the (agricultural) Extension Service. I believe all County Extension Services in the USA support a "Master Gardener" program. The Extension Service is a marvelous program that really helps people. The Master Gardener program is staffed by volunteers that are expert gardeners and should be able to answer all of your questions about growing "tomatoes", "eggplants" or "peppers" in your local climate. The plants mentioned above have very similar growth requirements to cannabis. In fact, if you have the time and the inclination, sign up for the Master Gardener program in Dayton. I guarantee you will learn much more in this program than you will by talking to a couple of farmers. You also might want to stop by the local nursery and ask several nursery people about growing in the area.

THE BUCK STOPS HERE!

Dear Jorge,

I have been growing five years and had only one problem, deer! This year I started with 28 seedlings, and by the middle of the summer, I had four plants left! I tried mothballs and dog hair as a deterrent. I talked to other growers in the area, and they are having the same problems. Help us save all our crops!

Captain Hook, Northeast Georgia

Dear Captain,

I always heard Georgia deer were the friendliest in the world! Deer live in a relatively small area and know it well. Once they have found your patch, you can bet they will be by every evening to browse. Deer repellents either frighten the beasts or make wonderful weed unappealing to their taste buds. You have tried frightening them with the scent of mothballs and dog hair, but your application rate could be askew. According to one of our loyal readers, "to keep wild animals from eating your crop, go to the barbershop, collect human hair, and spread it around your crop. Reapply once a month to keep a fresh scent." Other solutions include urinating around the patch on every visit and hanging wet bags of blood meal from the trees.

Deer get used to people and dogs fast. After 8-foot fences, your best bet is to make the plants taste bad. Go to your local retail nursery and ask the clerk for a product like Deer Away that repels deer. Or make a 2 percent solution of Tabasco spray. Apply as often as needed.

PLANT NOW!

Dear Jorge,

First of all, I'm sorry for my bad English. I hope you will tell me the exact days to put the seeds directly under the ground for outdoor cultivation, obviously, in the flat peninsula at the extreme southeast of Italy. Many thanks, a lot of grass.

Geggè Campi Salentina, Italy

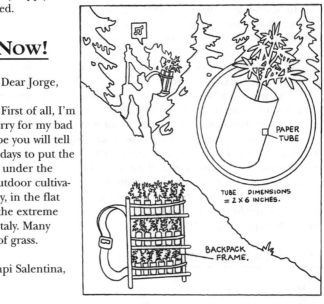

PAPER TUBE

TUBE DIMENSIONS = 2 X 6 INCHES.

BACKPACK FRAME.

Geggè,

You live in the tip of the Italian continental boot at the 38th parallel. You are entering the end of the growing season but, your latitude and mild marine climate you can grow outdoors all year round! The sun is not as bright and shines fewer hours per day, but you can still harvest small plants early next year. You can start seeds, but you are best to start them in pots in full sun and transplant. Plant a few more clones or seedlings than you would in the spring. Plants and buds will be smaller, but they still smoke the same! Plant in full sun and remember the angle of the sun is lower now and finding full sun locations is a bit more demanding.

LIGHT
HOW MANY LIGHTS?

Dear Jorge,

Economics aside, which lighting configuration would be best for my 5 x 5 x7-foot closet garden? I have a 4 x 4-foot ebb & flow garden and the ballasts would be outside the garden and the reflectors would be air-cooled.

Sincerely J.T., Central Texas

Dear J.T.,

A 600w HPS generates 92,000 lumens and a pair of 400w HIDs about 90,000 while consuming more electricity. But these simple facts tell only part of the story. The extra blue from a 400w metal halide combined with the red-orange spectrum of 400w HPS yield a more balanced spectrum causing less internodal stretching between branches. A 400w lamp also burns cooler and can be placed closer to plants. Since light fades exponentially fast, the closer a bulb can be to plants without burning them, the brighter. For example, the 400s can be about 6 inches closer to plants than a 600w bulb. Two sources of light will spread the light more evenly over your plants. Make sure to buy an inexpensive light meter to measure the output of light under the two HIDs so that you get the most even distribution of light. Two lamps

A Sun Twist™ moves bulbs in circles above plants increasing the bright light plants receive from many different angles.

also afford you flexibility. Sometimes you will need to use only one lamp, such as the first two weeks when plants are small and unable to process as much light. Or, you may want to divide the closet into two rooms, upper and lower. You could have a lamp for each room.

Light strength diminishes exponentially as it moves away from the source.

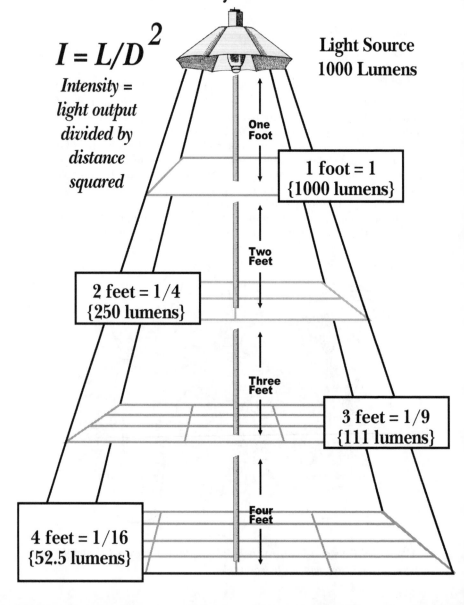

$$I = L/D^2$$

Intensity = light output divided by distance squared

Light Source
1000 Lumens

One Foot

1 foot = 1
{1000 lumens}

Two Feet

2 feet = 1/4
{250 lumens}

Three Feet

3 feet = 1/9
{111 lumens}

Four Feet

4 feet = 1/16
{52.5 lumens}

Cannabis Clue:

Buy the entire HID system: ballast, lamp, socket, bulb, connecting
wiring and timer all at the same time from a reputable supplier to
ensure the ballast and lamp go together. Make sure to get a written
guarantee from the dealer.

TOO MUCH LIGHT?

Dear Jorge,

I have two grow rooms one with a 600w HP sodium and a 1000w
Hortilux HP sodium on a rotating system which I use for flowering. The other room is smaller and I have a 400w metal halide
light that I use for vegetation. Do I need to have more light in the smaller
room? Is it bad to switch the plants from 400w to 1600w after vegetation? Also
if I use CO_2, what can I expect for maximum yield using these lights.

Please help,

J. Blaze, Milwaukee, WI

Dear J.,

A one-to-four ratio (400w to 1600w) is right on. Plants in the
vegetative stage are smaller and require less light than flowering
plants. To get the most efficiency from watts used, huddle small vegetative
plants together under the 400w metal halide and keep the lamp from 12 to
18 inches above the plants, which increases light intensity exponentially.
Flowering plants need more light to develop dense compact buds. As long as
lamps are not so close they burn foliage, all is well. Lamps on a (ceiling)
rotating system such as the Sun Twist moves lamps overhead so they can be
placed closer to foliage. For example, a 600w HP sodium that yields 80,000
lumens one foot from the source also produces one quarter as much light,
20,000 lumens, two feet away!

Although effective during flowering, higher CO_2 levels increase vegetative
growth the most. As a general rule of thumb, adding up to 1500-PPM (parts
per million) of CO_2 to the atmosphere increases overall yield about 20 percent when all other needs of the plant are met to the fullest.

SKYLIGHT & SKINNY STEMS

Hi Jorge,

I am a first time grower and there is so much information in your growing guide that I am a little fuzzy. I recently started 13 plants and all of them died. I used half potting soil and half topsoil in a 14-inch diameter pot with 5 inches deep of this mixture of soil. The plants were growing nicely, but then began to become spindly. I had them in my bathroom that has a skylight and I watered them about once a week.

I am not sure what happened to them and was wondering if you could give me any insight.

Thank You

Jul N. Cyberspace

Dear Jul,

Direct sunlight decreases by about 25 percent when it must pass through a window before finding foliage. If the sun passes directly over the house, the plants would receive direct light for no more than a couple of hours daily. All other light would be indirect and not as intense. Plants grow spindly with long slender stems when they are groping for light. The problem is compounded when soil drainage is poor and soil is clayey. Using outdoor topsoil probably decreased drainage and held water too long, which may have caused damping off, a condition where plants rot at the soil line.

Start plants again in a deeper pot and use only potting soil. Buy at least a 65w compact fluorescent lamp or something bigger, such as a 250w HID. Put plants under the lamp and forget about the skylight, it does not supply enough light for rapid sustained growth.

SMALL LIGHTS, BIG BUDS

Dear Jorge,

Can I buy a 150w HP sodium yard lamp at the local hardware store to grow herb? I am too paranoid to go into a grow store or order through the mail.

Curious, Alberta, Canada

Dear Curious,

    Sure you can use a 150w HP sodium yard lamp to grow herb.
However, you may want to change the reflective hood because yard lamps are
designed to illuminate a large area when mounted at a height of 12 to 20
feet. The reflective hood/fixture will need to be placed about a foot above
plants. You may need to build your own reflector.

    A grower from Iowa used 150w lamps in conjunction with a 1000w HP sodi-
um. The buds were bigger than if the 150w lamps were used exclusively. The
bulbs were mounted vertically in the fixture and light is baffled by a protective Plexiglas covering. Vertical orientation and the Plexiglas reduce light
transmission substantially.

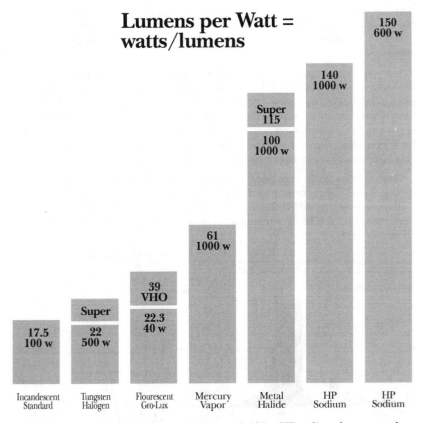

Lumens per Watt = watts/lumens

							150 600 w
						140 1000 w	
					Super 115		
					100 1000 w		
				61 1000 w			
		39 VHO					
	Super	22.3 40 w					
17.5 100 w	22 500 w						
Incandescent Standard	Tungsten Halogen	Flourescent Gro-Lux	Mercury Vapor	Metal Halide	HP Sodium	HP Sodium	

*Incandescent bulbs are the least efficient and 600w HP sodium lamps are the
most efficient. The brightest bulbs measured in lumens per watt are the metal
halide and HP sodium bulbs.*

More Light

I am growing one 'Blueberry' plant and need to know how many watts would I need to get a good yield out of a 2-4-foot plant? What kind of light is better, a HID, a metal halide or a HP sodium? When you take clones from a mother, can you take clones of those clones and still have an F1 plant? Or would you have to keep taking clones from a mother?

Thanks
A. D. K., Seattle, WA

Dear A.,

'Blueberry' is a wonderful variety. Excellent choice! The number of watts is contingent upon the type of lamp. If you use either type of HID lamp, metal halide or HP sodium, you should need no more than 250 watts to grow a 3 foot tall plant. However, you can grow 3-4 such plants with the same 250w bulb. Using a single bulb to grow a single plant wastes a lot of light. The same wattage of HP sodium and MH lamps are virtually par.

You can continue to take clones from the clones of an original mother and the same genetic qualities of the original mother plant persist. The mother plant (and clones) will retain the genetic integrity for many generations as long as they are always kept in the vegetative growth stage. When a mother or clone enters flowering stage with a 12/12 day/night photoperiod, and reverts back to vegetative growth with a 18/6 day/night photoperiod, genetic integrity is lost forever. Plants become weaker and less potent.

Clones do not grow as robustly as original F1 seed. F1 hybrids are the offspring of two "true breeding" parents. F1 hybrid seed exhibits "hybrid vigor", a characteristic that makes them grow about 25 percent faster and bigger than other plants. This "hybrid vigor" is greatly diminished or lost when clones are taken.

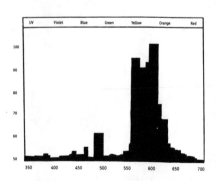

The color spectrum of HP sodium lamps is concentrated in the yellow/orange range.

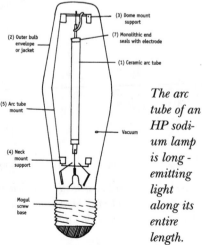

The arc tube of an HP sodium lamp is long - emitting light along its entire length.

Jorge's Rx:

Santa Claus laughed, even though two elephants perused subways, but two Macintoshes bought putrid bureaux.Mark gossips. Umpteen Five pawnbrokers untangles Darin. The obese Jabberwocky gossips.

AN

ACUTE PERCEPTION

My guess would be that the odds of you answering this question are considerably less than me being struck by lightning before I finish writing this letter (and I'm on the ground floor of a large building on a sunny day), but I'll ask anyway as a sort of Zen exercise.

If you're growing the right strains indoors, and you've got 65 watts per square foot of HPS light, can you increase the yield by spreading the plants out so you've got only 50 watts per square foot?

That would be 30% more area, but 23% less light. I know HIGH TIMES says the yield would be about equal, with at least slightly better quality with brighter light, but whenever you guys discuss this you're just about always talking about the difference between 20 and 40 watts per square foot.

Obviously there's a point of diminishing returns in cramming the plants as close together as possible. Otherwise, why not use HALF the area, and grow under 130 watts per square foot? Because the plants can only use so much light, AND the closer together the plants are, the more they block each others' light.

Using light movers and air-cooled reflector hoods allows you to put 1000w lights only 1 foot above the plants, so 50 watts per square foot of HPS light should still give you over 5000 foot-candles, which should be plenty bright for Indica and mostly-Indica plants.

Yeah, it's true that 70 or 80 watts per square foot will grow much bigger individual buds than 50 watts per square foot, but it's the TOTAL yield that's important.

Besides, my experience is that huge buds aren't the way to go. Light only penetrates so far into the interior of a huge bud. The interior of huge buds tend to be leafy, and compared to leaves growing on the surface of buds, interior leaves tend to be lighter in color (having less chlorophyll) and more "ruffled" (less flat), and most importantly, have FAR fewer glandular trichomes.

I'm interested in finding out one specific thing: the difference in yield for Indica-type plants grown under 50 and 65 watts per square foot.

Thanks,

Anslinger's Dead

Dear Anslinger's Dead,

I love your name!

Let's see, 65 watts per square foot of HPS light that would be one 1000w HPS hung over an area that measures about 4 x 4-feet, and 50 watts per square foot would be one 1000w HPS over a 4.5 x 4.5-foot area. Dude, either way the light is blinding!

First thing I would do is find the brightest light you can. A 600w HPS that has a lumen-per-watt (LPW) conversion of 150, the highest per watt of any commercially available HID lamp. The LPW conversion of a 1000w HPS is 140, 7 percent less than the 600w. Next I would hang this lamp over an area measuring 4 x 4 feet and use every last bit of know-how you possess to grow the absolute best plants possible.

Your plants will produce less leaf and more bud under 65 watts-per-square foot, but a very similar net harvest of dry buds. Watts per square foot does not account for how much light is received by plants. Other factors such as how far the lamp is away from the plants, the efficiency of the lamp and the reflector and the point source of illumination are not factored into the equation either.

After doing the research on my book, *Marijuana Indoors: Five Easy Gardens*, I'm not in agreement with the yield being "about" equal when the proper lamp is used. In fact, the yield of dried bud per watt every 60 days drops like a rock! A healthy yield with 1000w bulb is two pounds (908 grams) in the area. Divide 908 by 1000 to find grams per watt (GPW). 908/1000 = 0.908 GPW. Changing the bulb to 600 watts will drop the watts per square-foot to 40 and cause the harvest to fall about 20 percent, (726 grams) but the grams per watt increases to 1.36 (726/600 = 1.21 GPW) about 20 percent more.

Safety Tip:
Mix dry soilless amendments outdoors and wear a respirator.

SOIL

GOOD DIRT

Dear Jorge,

I have heard that if the right soil mixture is used, fertilization isn't necessary until the flowering stage. I understood that while in the vegetative stage, watering is only necessary if using the perfect vermiculite/perlite mix with inert soil conditioners added. Is this true or have I heard wrong? If so, where can I go about obtaining more information on this subject?

The Frizzler

Dear Frizzler,

Yes, it is true that no "supplemental" fertilization is necessary when adequate nutrients are added to the initial soil mixture. Common additives to soil mixes are manures including guano, kelp meal, bone meal, blood meal and numerous other organic fertilizers. Many organic soil mixes contain enough fertilizer to supply plants with nutrients for a month or more of vegetative growth. Many soilless mixes are "fortified" with fertilizer that supply nutrients to plants for a month or longer.

An inert substance will not react with another substance. Fertilizers are not inert because they react with plants. A soil conditioner improves the texture of the soil so it retains water and still drains. The perlite/vermiculite mix is a soilless mix. A soilless mix contains no organic material.

When purchasing soil or soilless mix, always read the information on the bag. Purchase the product at a nursery or garden center with knowledgeable personnel that are able to explain your questions in language you understand and can use.

REUSING SOILLESS MIX

Jorge,

Is it OK to use soilless mix twice as long as I leach it well with a mild bleach solution?

MP, Milwaukee, WI

Dear MP,

Sure you can use soilless mix as many times as you want, but you are open-ing the door for lots of problems, even if it is sterilized. Once used, soilless mix or potting mix looses a good deal of the fluff in its texture and compacts more, which excludes necessary oxygen. Roots need oxygen to take in nutri-ents. While sterilizing with bleach kills disease pathogens, pests and their eggs, it is not always completely effective and soil-borne disease is much more common. Saving a few bucks and a little time by not replacing your growing medium could cost much more in lost harvest and "fix-it" time.

Jorge's Rx:

Soilless mixes are the preferred substrate for many bedding plant and vegetable seedling commercial growers. The commercial mixes are regaining ground against soil and other hydroponic mediums. Successful growers know that soilless mixes have good texture, hold water and drain well. Unless fortified, soilless mixes contain no nutrients and are pH balanced near 6.0 – 7.0. Coarse soilless mixes drain well and are easy to push plants into growing faster with heavy fertilization. The fast-draining mixes can be leached efficiently so nutrients have little chance of building up to toxic levels. Look for ready-mixed bags of fortified soilless mixes such as Jiffy Mix®, Ortho Mix®, Sunshine Mix®, Terra-Lite®, etc. To improve drainage, mix 10 – 30 percent coarse perlite before planting. Fortified ele-ments supply nutrients up to a month. I still recommend using a complete fertilizer designed for hydroponics that contains chelated trace elements.

LIME

Dear Jorge,

What is the best way to tell how much lime to add to my soil mix? I use Earth Juice, which lowers my pH to about 4. The pH of the water is 6.7. The acidic nutrient causes my leaves to curl and burn. I don't want to add pH UP, because the crop will not be organic.

Burnt in the Closet

You have a pH problem for sure! One thing I would definitely do is go to the Earth Juice web site www.greenfire.net, or give them a call at their Sacramento, CA store. Tell them you are growing toma-toes or peppers or some other annual vegetable in containers. They must have this problem of low pH in growing mediums all the time. They would be best suited to answer the question specifically.

My take on the problem is to throw in three quarters cup of dolomite lime flower (the finest grade) and one-quarter cup hydrated lime for every cubic foot of soil. Dolomite lime breaks down slowly and is difficult to over-apply. Hydrated lime is very fast acting and easy to overapply. I would not add more than the above dosage.

The lime mix should buffer your soil mix and raise the pH of the chemistry.

Correcting the pH of the soil and nutrient should solve the toxic nutrient problems. You should also leach the containers out by pouring two or three gallons in containers for each gallon of soil. A 5-gallon container would get 15 gallons of water. Leaching will help correct pH and wash out any salt build-up.

CONTAINERS

WHITE POTS

 Jorge,

If black pots make roots too hot on a summer day, why don't they make the pots white to stay cooler and reflect heat?

Bright Bud

Dear Bud,

Good point. Many pots are white and they do just that, reflect hot sun. A black pot can heat to excess of 140 degrees F in just a few minutes! That's guaranteed to fry the root system in no time. If you want to protect the root system even more, you could shade the pot with a piece of wood or another container. Keeping the root system cool is one of the biggest problems when growing in containers.

Containers must be:

Clean
Have adequate drainage holes
Big enough to accommodate the plant

Container Shape, Size and Maintenance

Popular pot shapes include rectangular and cylindrical. Growers prefer taller pots rather than wide squat containers because the cannabis root system penetrates deeply. Of all the gardens I have visited, squat pots were few and far between. Growers I queried said they may hold more soil for their stature, but did not produce as extensive of a root system.

The volume of a container can easily dictate the size of a plant. Cannabis is an annual, grows very fast and requires a lot of root space for sustained vigorous development. Containers should be big enough to allow for a strong root system, but be just big enough to contain the root system before harvest. If the container is too small, roots are confined, water and nutrient uptake is limited and growth slows to a crawl. But if the container is too big, it requires too much expensive growing medium and becomes heavy and awkward to move.

Marijuana roots develop and elongate quickly, growing down and out, away from the main taproot. For example, about midsummer nurseries have unsold tomato plants that are still in small 4-inch and one-gallon containers. The stunted plants have blooming flowers and ripe fruit. But few branches extend much beyond the sides of the container; the plants are tall and leggy with curled down leaves and an overall stunted sickly appearance. These plants are pot or root-bound. Once a plant deteriorates to this level, it is often easier and more efficient to toss it out and replace it with a healthy one.

Roots soon hit the sides of containers where they grow down and matt up around the bottom. The unnatural environment inside the container often causes a thick layer of roots to grow alongside the container walls and bottom. This portion of the root zone is the most vulnerable to moisture and heat stress and is the most exposed!

ROOT BOUND

Dear Jorge,

I am growing two strains. This is my seventh crop. My buds are tight and dense, but they could be a little tighter. I thought maybe the roots are pot bound. When plants were budding three weeks, I cut the bottom off of their three-gallon pots and found a wall of roots with nowhere to grow. I put it in another pot filled with clean soil, perlite and vermiculite. Now they are exploding. The buds are much heavier and extremely healthy. Each plant is two feet tall with six to eight super-cropped branches. I keep it simple and organic.

Thank you for an awesome column.

Moso, Cyberspace

Dear Moso,

You have unearthed a very deep subject, roots. Some varieties have bigger root systems than others; most often sativa and predominately sativa/indica

Soil   Air   Water

This cut away drawing shows how roots penetrate soil. Note there must be enough air trapped in the soil to allow biological activity and absorption of nutrients.

crosses. In general, tall bushy plants have bigger root systems. Plants with large root systems require more root space. Healthy plants grow more roots as they mature. You may want to induce flowering a little earlier, say when the plants are about 6 inches tall, to keep them from becoming so root bound that it inhibits growth.

Cultural practices can also increase roots propensity to become pot bound. For example, roots grow in loose growing soil rapidly stretching out and touching the sides and bottom. When roots run out of space, they circle sides and the bottom of the pot. The problem is, very few roots grow in theinterior soil. Check this when you harvest by breaking the soil open to see where the roots are. My guess is about 80 percent of them will be circling the pot. Get more roots to grow in the interior of the soil by transplanting twice after cloning. First transplant the rooted cutting into a 4-inch container. This way a strong root system develops within the small space. Transplant the 4-inch pot into a 3-gallon container when the plant is 6 – 8 inches tall and induce flowering.

Cannabis Clue:

Plants process tepid (70 – 80 degrees F) water rapidly and it penetrates the growing medium more easily. Tepid water does not shock tender root hairs or leaves.

Jorge's Rx

WATER

SWEET WATER

Jorge,

I purchased the *Indoor Bible* and still need to know if I can use distilled water to lower the chance of salt buildup. I grow indoors using the Quick Grow system, www.quickgrow.ca.

J. B., Cyberspace

Super Size Secret:

Run water with more than 300 PPM dissolved solids through a reverse osmosis machine.

Dear J. B.

The mobile QuickGrow system is one of several new "grow boxes" that have become popular. It measures a compact 72 x 48 x 26 inches and the top chamber is lit with 26,000 lumens in a 36 x 48 x 26-inch area, about 8 square feet of actual growing area. You can use distilled water exclusively and lower your incidence of toxic salt buildup, but remember, you will also pay about $0.50 for each gallon. You could easily use 20 gallons a week, increasing your cost by about $40 per month. You will also have to schlep it in. One gallon of water weighs about 8 pounds.

If your source water contains more than 300 PPM (parts per million) dissolved solids, you may have a problem. Request a water analysis from your local water bureau, or check your water with an EC (electrical conductivity), DS (dissolved solids) TDS (total dissolved solids) or CF (conductivity factor) meter – all measure the total dissolved solids in the water and give you a gross readout.

If the sum of the total dissolved solids (calcium, magnesium, sodium, etc.) exceeds 300 PPM, the dissolved solids level is too high. You must decrease your nutrient mix or start with cleaner water. Sodium is the worst dissolved solid. In quantities above 50 PPM, roots absorb sodium instead of other dissolved solids (fertilizer).

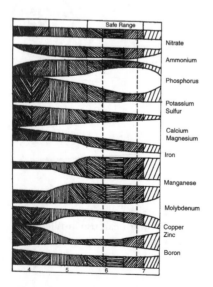

Solutions include mixing distilled water 50/50 with tap water to dilute the dissolved solids PPM from 300 to 150. Purchase an inexpensive RO machine such as the Spectrum from $250 - $300 for models that produce 30 – 50 gallons of clean water daily.

This pH chart shows the "Safe Zone" is between 5.8 and 6.8.

An inexpensive electronic pH tester is easy to use.

PURE WATER

Mr. Cervantes,
I recently ran across a large electromagnetic water purification device. I have seen smaller ones available and I doubted their abilities. This is a large home and commercial size units. Keep up the great work and never stop fighting for your and my rights.

A loyal admirer of yours,

Glenn, Arizona

Dear Glenn,
I called a couple of big growers in Australia and one in Spain, both arid countries with exceptionally bad water – high pH full of calcium and other dissolved solids that create nutrient lockout problems for hydroponic growers. None of them use an electrostatic machine. The Australians are using reverse osmosis (RO) machines to clean water of salts before using it in their hydroponic systems and the Spanish grower uses nothing to treat his water. The Spanish grower grows in soil and flushes it heavily every watering and letting at least twenty five percent of the irrigation water run out the bottom of the container to flush away excess salts.

The Electromagnetic machine sends radio waves into the water causing free electrons to reduce the hydrogen bonding between dissolved solids molecules. The bonding keeps salts and other minerals in solution. The amount of dissolved salts diminishes substantially, but it does not disappear.

Reverse osmosis, known as hyper-filtration, the finest filtration known, is a process that filters out virtually all of the dissolved solids in water. Dissolved solids (salts) cause problems in irrigation water because the salts act as fertilizers. Water with a high level of calcium has a high pH and is common in dry low rainfall areas. Other dissolved solids such as sodium and magnesium cause other elements to be locked up in the nutrient solution and become unavailable to plants even though they are in abundant supply.

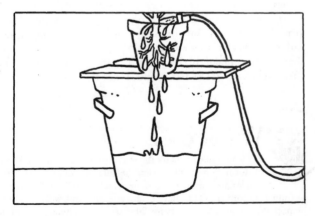

Flushing plants with plain water will wash out most built up toxic salts. Flush again with a dilute nutrient solution.

NUTRIENTS

NEED SERIOUS HELP
BEFORE IT'S TOO LATE

I have two big Buddha females that are 10 weeks old. I forced flowered them at 8 weeks. I'm using 400w HPS and my mixture is Schultz's (10-60-10) in rockwool and perlite. Now the tips of the leaves are turning yellow, then brown and they're curling upwards. I'm in a state of panic because this will be my only source of income due to a disability. The book I was reading said to treat with Epsom salts. It also said if the mixture contains magnesium do not use Epsom salts! What to do? I leached the soil and used Epsom salts several times. I disconnected the water supply thinking it may be over-fertilization, reconnected because not sure. Scared don't know what to do... please help

I await your reply.
Thank you.

Paid Cyberbud, Boston, MA

Dear Cyberbud,

For sure there is a magnesium deficiency, which is exhibited by yellowing between the leaf veins, and tips curl up. But there are other problems too. Did the yellowing start on the older leaves and progress up the plant? If so, this means the deficiency is confined to the "mobile" elements (nitrogen, phosphorous, potassium, zinc and magnesium), which is probably the case. If the rockwool was not "conditioned" the pH will be too high and nutrient absorption will be impaired. Condition rockwool by soaking in an acidic solution overnight. Check the pH of the nutrient solution and the runoff solution to ensure the pH is consistent. They should be between 5.8 and 6.5. Leach growing medium with a mild nutrient solution specifically made for hydroponics such as General, Genesis, NutraLife, Dutch Magic, etc. These mixes are very soluble and contain all necessary nutrients in a balanced available form. The fertilizer you are using is not made for this application. Gain some patience. Overreacting compounds problems. Plants respond slowly to changes. It will take three to four days for a change in fertilizer regimen to affect the plant. For fastest results, foliar feed plants.

Jorge's Canna Coco

I would like to thank the scientists at Canna Coco, Breda, Netherlands, for information about nutrient deficiencies and toxicities in cannabis. Canna is the largest supplier of indoor growing medium, fertilizers and biological products in Europe. They have been experimenting with cannabis in their fully equipped scientific laboratory for 20 years. Mauk, head scientist, has made numerous discovers about the nutrition needs of cannabis that he has proved scientifically. Hit their web site!!! www.canna.com.

BRITTLE LEAVES

Dear Jorge,

The leaves on my plants are weird. Some are dark purple and others are dark green. They don't grow very fast and they are in the fifth week of budding. I fertilize them with a hydroponic fertilizer and

they are growing in Sunshine mix. I tried to leach out the extra fertilizer like you say to do, but it doesn't make much difference. The leaves are still dark colored and brittle.

Bummed out in BC

This prize was won by Hesi Fertilizers at the 2002 Highlife Hemp Expo in Holland.

Dear Bummed,

Pour a gallon of water through one of those pots. Measure the EC and the pH of the input water and the EC and the pH of the water that drains out the bottom of the pot. This simple test will tell you if the runoff water is packed with fertilizer that was never absorbed by the plant. When you continue to add acidic fertilizer to a soil or soilless mix, it continues to acidify the mix. Around the fourth week of flowering, the pH is usually so low that nutrient uptake is severely restricted. Leaching does not always increase the pH. The solution is to raise the pH of the nutrient to 6 or 7 so that it can be absorbed in such an acidic environment. One of the best places to get right-on advice about growing and this subject specifically is from Larry at THC-BC, Tel. 1-604-685-4769. This guy really knows his shit and will share his extensive background of knowledge, based on hands-on experience, with you.

FERTILIZER BURN

Dear Jorge,

I am growing 'Northern Lights' x 'Big Bud.' The week after I fertilize, I think my plants have fertilizer burn. The leaf tips and edges are burned. I use Miracle-Gro for Tomatoes (18-18-21) for vegetative growth and Miracle-Grow 15-30-15 for flowering.

Thanks Jorge!

Thom, West Virginia

Dear Thom,

The cross you are growing should yield heavily when fertilized properly. Remedy your problem by flushing pots with 2-3 gallons of eighth-strength fertilizer for each gallon of growing medium. Switch to a high quality organic or hydroponic fertilizer. I'm always amazed that growers spend all kinds of time and money to secure the best seeds in the world and fertilize it with an inexpensive fertilizer. Always use a high quality organic or hydroponic fertilizer and follow their instructions carefully. When you have problems with fertilization, go back to the vendor and ask for specific recommendations. The vendor should have experience using the fertilizer they recommend.

PUNY PLANT!

Dear Jorge,

I've grown my plant for about two months and its barely 6 inches tall with only a couple of leaves. What is wrong? This is the only plant I have this year due to bad seeds.

Hammerhead, Cyberspace

Dear Hammerhead,

Bad seed grows bad plants. Couple grungy genetics with poor cultural practices and puny plants result. I'm guessing you are not using store-bought potting soil and the plant probably has suffered dry conditions too. It could have been stunted from excessive (fertilizer) salts in the irrigation water. For whatever reason, the plant has been stunted and should be tossed out. It could take several months to resume normal growth, and it might always be a runt. Start over with descent seed, good soil and don't over-fertilize.

PURPLE STEM?

Hello.
Could you please tell me about "Purple Stem." Is it just what it sounds like? Purple looking stems? What causes it? How do you get rid of it?

Thank you for your help.

Musicman, MO

Intervenal chlorosis, burned tips and some margins of older leaves, small stunted dark green new growth were all caused by excessive salts. NOTE: the line of toxic white salt around container lip.

Dear Musicman,

Purple stems are caused by genetic traits in some plants. Their stems and occasionally their flowers are naturally purple. But in many cases, the "purple stem" is caused by an excess of nitrogen and phosphorous. This excess causes stems, branches, leaf stems (petioles) and main leaf veins to turn reddish-purple. Nitrogen and phosphorus deficient plants accumulate anthocyanin, which turns them a reddish-purple color. When purple stems are accompanied by older mature bottom leaves that yellow between veins, a nitrogen deficiency is evident. When "purple stem" is found on a plant that has small, dark blue-green leaves, a phosphorous deficiency is obvious. Advanced symptoms of phosphorous deficiency include: lower leaf tips burn and often curl down.

Overcome these deficiencies by flushing out your growing medium with a weak nutrient solution and apply a complete soluble hydroponic fertilizer. You may also want to try some growth additives that promote nitrogen and phosphorus uptake. Contact any hydroponic store for more information on growth additives.

LEACHING
SAVE MY BABIES!

Jorge,

Hey man, I need your help. I've got some plants growing indoors and three of them have developed light brown spots on some of the leaves. One already died. They're about two weeks old and about 4 inches tall. I'm assuming they're fertilizer burned, but I've only used the Miracle Gro mix with water. I have them growing in a cooler over some flouros and only want to grow them a foot tall and flower them. Is there anything I can do now to save them?

Thanks

Smokey J., Tennessee Mountains

Flush excess fertilizer (salt build-up) from pots every month. Flush pots with at least two gallons of water for each gallon of soil.

Smokey,

You got it right. Two weeks is about long enough for the fertilizer to build up to toxic levels. Do you have any drainage holes in the cooler?

Remedy problem by cutting three, one-half inch drainage holes for every square foot of container bottom. Flush the toxic nutrients from the soil. Place containers in a deep sink and let plain water flush the container for about 5 minutes each. Next water with 1/8 strength Miracle Gro every other watering. The plants might have to grow about two months after this treatment to become strong enough to produce a decent crop of buds.

SALT BURN

Jorge,

Please help my pot! The leaves are burning at the edges. The leaves are also curling down and look wrinkled. Can you help my pot?

Bayou Pot Man

Mr. Pot Man,

You have the most common problem that plague growers, toxic fertilizer (salt) buildup in the soil. There are a lot of reasons for too much salt in your soil. A pH above 7.5 or below 5.5, saline water, water full of dissolved (salt) solids, and over-fertilization come to mind first. I could go on and on about this problem, but it's easier to just give you a simple solution. Flush the soil with three gallons of water for every gallon of soil. This will flush out all toxic salts and plants will resume healthy growth. New healthy growth will sprout in about a week. Do not fertilize plants for a couple of weeks. And when you do fertilize, make sure at least 20 percent of the water you pour into the pot drains out the bottom.

FERTILIZER
BEST OF EVERYTHING

Jorge,

What is the best soil mixture (in ratios or parts)? What is the best fertilizer? What is the highest yielding strain? I know it is about genetics and environment, but there are so many strains to choose from. If you want to taste some of the best buds in North America, come to Montreal. Americans try our budz and they all say the same: MONTEREAL BUDZ are the BEST they ever had!

Thanks,
Ja Swan, Montreal, Quebec

Switzerland

Jorge's RX

U ntil the legal crackdown that started in the fall of 2002, Switzerland was the new Mecca for marijuana growing. An anonymous grower shows off a field of clones that is about to be harvested. Many growers prefer female clones to seeds. Clones grow smaller and produce less than if grown from seed. They are easier to harvest and produce a higher bud to leaf ratio too. Learn more about growing in Switzerland at www.cannatrade.ch.

SOIL GARDENS

Spain

1 - Expert grower Xus inspects a few of the plants in his garden. The brick wall acts as a heat bank.

Spain

2 - Bending branches laterally helps sunshine penetrate the entire plant and develop larger buds.

2

FRANCE

3 - Guard dogs are commonplace in marijuana gardens around the world.

3

4

4 - You can expect anything when planting seeds of unknown origin. This Swiss plant produced a four-foot tall bud!

5 - Legal Dutch plants are in full view of a grade school located just 50 feet beyond the balcony. The grower moves plants inside at night so they receive 12 hours of darkness daily, buds are harvested in late August.

Switzerland

Holland

5

Holland

Jorge's RX

1 - Planting cannabis in a cornfield provides natural cover from thieves. This Swiss grower planted on one end of the cornfield to obscure plants from a nearby highway.

2 - This grower bent branches downward so light was able to penetrate more deeply into the plant in this backyard garden in Amsterdam, Holland.

3 - Close-up of greenhouse-grown bud several weeks from harvest shows that you can grow incredibly good quality nugs under plastic or glass.

4 - This expert cultivator found that a high water table and residual nutrients in the soil made it unnecessary to irrigate or fertilize! The consistency and quality of the crop proved him to be right.

Switzerland

Switzerland

5 - Crops of clones are much easier to manage when growing under glass. This grower avoids many problems by growing short plants. The rule of thumb for greenhouses is to have one third of the cubic space filled with plants and two thirds filled with air.

SEEDS & SEEDLINGS

1 - Soak seeds overnight in plain water. In general, seeds that sink to the bottom have a higher percentage of viability.

2 - Next, sandwich seeds between a moist paper towel on a dinner plate. Drain away excess water. Keep towel evenly moist.

3 - Seeds will sprout a white taproot in a day or three.

4 - Some growers prefer to soak seeds overnight in water and plant directly in a root cube.

5 - Seedling starts to emerge after a few days.

6 - Seedling with first signs of "true leaves" seen between rounded cotyledon or seed leaves.

7 - Seedling with long taproot in rockwool.

8 - Sprouted seedling shows rounded cotyledon leaves and serrated true leaves.

SEX

Male

Female

ove: Distinguish male plants early by identi-
ng the small nub at branch union. The nub
nost always turns into male flowers. Look for
sign after two months of growth.

low: The nub soon turns into a male flower
at looks like a small tapered pod. This pod or
llen sack is packed with fine microscopic
ains of male pollen. Upon opening, the pollen
dispersed. Female plants in the vicinity will
come pollinated and start to pro-
ce seeds. In general male plants
ow taller and have less
iage than females.
ok for male character-
ics two or three
nths after planting.

Above: Female plants normally grow two
small white hairs from branch nodes. The
white hairs appear after about two months
of growth.

Below: Female plants generally grow more
squat and bushy than males. Dense flower
tops begin to form after the onset of white
pistils. Indoors, female pistils are clearly
evident two weeks after plants receive 12
hours of darkness and 12 hours of light
every 24 hours. Below is a healthy female
plant. The white hairs or pistils are
attached to a seed bract. When pollinated, a single grain of male pollen
slides down the pistils lodging in the
seed bract where a seed forms.

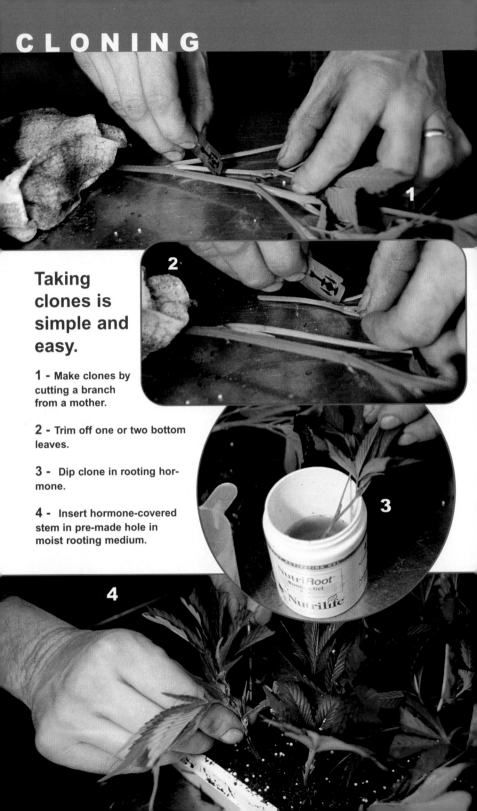

CLONING

Taking clones is simple and easy.

1 - Make clones by cutting a branch from a mother.

2 - Trim off one or two bottom leaves.

3 - Dip clone in rooting hormone.

4 - Insert hormone-covered stem in pre-made hole in moist rooting medium.

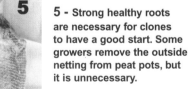

1 - A misting machine injects a fog of moisture into this cloning room increasing humidity to more than 95 percent. At inception clones have no roots to draw in water and nutrients. Increasing ambient humidity lowers moisture stress while expediting root growth.

2 - Rooting clones need minimal light and a warm humid environment. Strong healthy clones rooting in rockwool will be ready to transplant in 10-14 days.

3 - Clone Tech, a major Swiss clone producer, would make cuttings from the very center of the growing tip of a young robust F1 female. Once separated, the tips are grown and multiplied in auger solution. Resulting clones are exceptionally vigorous.

4 - The cloning room in the basement of this Swiss grow store was removed by police in the fall of 2002. They produced and sold thousands of clones every month. Growers could special order clones by telephone three weeks before picking them up.

5 - Strong healthy roots are necessary for clones to have a good start. Some growers remove the outside netting from peat pots, but it is unnecessary.

6 - The plant at right is well rooted and will grow into a strong vibrant female. A strong healthy root system on a robust plant is the key to a heavy harvest.

INDOOR GARDENS

Amsterdam's Cannabis College has a magnificent soil garden, indoors, and completely organic. This garden is open to the public daily!

Inset: A single plant grown from the Flying Dutchmen seed stock occupies almost all the space under a 400-watt HP sodium lamp.

JORGE'S Rx: Visit the Cannabis College and learn everything you can from the expert growers.

The Cannabis College, O.Z. Achterburgwal 124, 1012 Amsterdam, Netherlands, Tel. +31-20-423-4420, is one of my favorite places in the world. Any time you go to Amsterdam, this basement garden is a must-see. The well-trained staff can answer all of your cultivation and cannabis questions.

1 - Hanging lamps vertically with no reflector allows all the light to be dispersed into the room. Interestingly all plants in this room receive adequate light to grow well. After seeing this room along with many others, I believe that many growers give plants more light than they need.

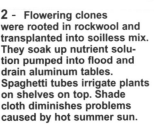

2 - Flowering clones were rooted in rockwool and transplanted into soilless mix. They soak up nutrient solution pumped into flood and drain aluminum tables. Spaghetti tubes irrigate plants on shelves on top. Shade cloth diminishes problems caused by hot summer sun.

3 - Small plastic-lined closet is home to a respectable garden that produces nearly a half-pound of dried tops every month. A single 400-watt lamp and plenty of fresh air are the pillars of this garden.

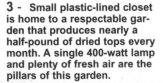

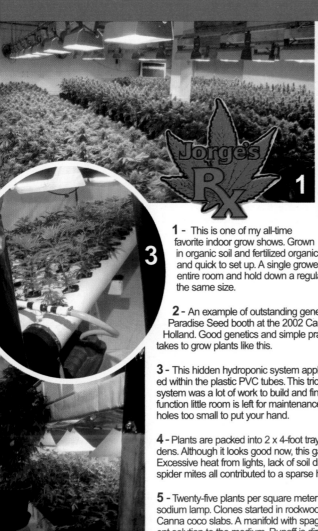

1 - This is one of my all-time favorite indoor grow shows. Grown in organic soil and fertilized organically, this garden was very simple and quick to set up. A single grower is able to take care of the entire room and hold down a regular day job. Notice all plants are the same size.

2 - An example of outstanding genetics was on display at the Paradise Seed booth at the 2002 Cannabis Cup in Amsterdam, Holland. Good genetics and simple pragmatic growing skill are all it takes to grow plants like this.

3 - This hidden hydroponic system applies nutrient via sprinklers located within the plastic PVC tubes. This tricked out homemade hydroponic system was a lot of work to build and fine-tune. If sprinklers clog or malfunction little room is left for maintenance. Note pots are inserted in holes too small to put your hand.

4 - Plants are packed into 2 x 4-foot trays and grown in shallow gardens. Although it looks good now, this garden produced poorly. Excessive heat from lights, lack of soil drainage and bumper crops of spider mites all contributed to a sparse harvest.

5 - Twenty-five plants per square meter grow below each 600-watt HP sodium lamp. Clones started in rockwool cubes were transplanted to Canna coco slabs. A manifold with spaghetti feeder tubes delivers nutrient solution to the medium. Runoff is directed to an outdoor garden.

6 - Simple clean and easy describes this Spanish indoor scene. Growers set up makeshift tables setting pots inside of different sized trays to catch runoff.

NUTRIENT PROBLEMS

1 - The clones on the left are potassium deficient evidenced by burned leaf margins. Remedy this problem by flushing soil with plenty of fresh clean water and keep the pH below 6.5.

2 - Damping off is generally caused by pythium wilt. This clone shows definite symptoms of rot on lower stem.

3 - The (white) salt buildup is evident on this container. Excess fertilizer salts in the nutrient solution and water built up on the outside of this pot. Imagine how much (fertilizer and native water) salt was built up in the growing medium. Imagine your baby's roots growing in such a salt-laden soil!

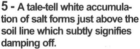

4 - This bud could be thick and heavy. With regular soil flushing this bud would produce 30-40 percent more mass and weight. Burned, hooked down discolored leaves are the sign of too much fertilizer and not enough drainage.

5 - A tale-tell white accumulation of salt forms just above the soil line which subtly signifies damping off.

6 - Yellow burned leaves signify this bud has been deprived of water, nitrogen and just about every other element necessary for strong healthy growth. The plant has been sick its entire life. Flushing toxic fertilizer away with water every 2-4 weeks would have increased yield substantially.

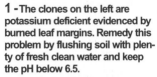

7 - Salt buildup is evident in the bottom of this net pot. As the nutrient solution flows through the slits, fertilizer salts have a chance to accumulate. It is white, just like table salt, but with a bit different consistency.

1 - Check the EC or PPM of the mild nutrient solution before leaching growing medium. Some growers prefer to use plain water while others use a mild nutrient solution. I suggest leaching with nutrient solution with an EC of 0.2 or a PPM reading of 100-150.

2 - Pour plenty of mild nutrient solution over the top of the container so that it penetrates the soil evenly. When growing medium is dry, irrigation water often runs down the side of the pot creating dry pockets of soil that never get water.

3 - This five-liter pot (1.3 gallons) is being leached with 15 liters (3.9 gallons) of mild nutrient solution. The container is removed from the red bucket as soon as all of the solution has been applied so that the excess can drain away freely.

4 - Take a EC or PPM reading of the runoff water to find out how much toxic (fertilizer) salt was washed from the growing medium. If the differential is more than 100-200 PPM, too much salt was in the growing medium.

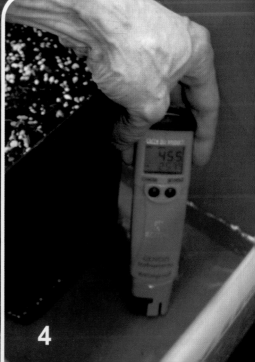

MEDICAL MARIJUANA

1 - Medical Marijuana Martyr, Ed Rosenthal, in an appearance at the 1997 Cannabis Cup in Amsterdam.

2 - Haze is my all time favorite variety and the favorite of countless connoisseurs. The quintessential incarnation of the soaring sativa high, this variety has been the mainstay of many visionaries. Haze is used medicinally as well.

3 - Indica buds have a stony effect on consumers. This type of stone lowers pressure and tension in the body and mind. Documented research supports these conclusions. www.arsec.es, and other sites.

4 - Translucent THC-rich resin is easy to see in this close up of a ripe indica bud.

5 - Notice most of the hair-like pistils in this close up photo have turned amber in color, which means this bud is ready to harvest!

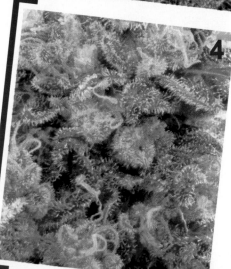

1 - The grower carefully trimmed this tightly packed indica bud just after harvesting.

2 - BC Big Bud is a favorite commercial variety in Canada. Although not the best THC producer, BC Big Bud is very easy to grow and produces a heavy harvest.

3 - Close up of dense compact bud shows that at least half of the white pistils have turned amber while half remain white. Many growers prefer to pick their plant now to get a lighter more flying stone.

4 - You can see animal hair on this bud. This grower had a cat that loved to be in the grow room. As the cat moved among the plants, it shed fur that was readily attracted by sticky resin. Smoking the hair is unpleasant and unnecessary. If using marijuana therapeutically, make sure to keep it free of fur!

5 - This plant still has a couple of weeks to go before harvest. Note that none of the white pistils have changed color to amber.

1
**- Want
to make buds
swell?** Crops gain
more weight and THC when plants are healthy.
Some varieties of plants can be pushed to
incredible extremes. Commercial bedding plant
growers have pushed plants to grow faster and
bigger by manipulating fertilizer regimens.

2 - Sensi Seeds set up this incredible display of
their varieties just for this photo. Plants in individual containers are easy to move around.

3 - These plants look great! Notice there are no
burnt or discolored leaves. This grower used
Canna's PK 13-14 during the last weeks of flowering. This product, available from many different manufacturers, adds soluble potassium and
phosphorus to produce firm compact buds.

4 - Inefficient light reflectors and lackadaisi-
cal attention to nutrient buildup diminished
the harvest in this room by at least 20 percent. A small investment in new reflectors
and paying closer attention to toxic salt
buildup are easy and worth the price.

Jorge's Rx

Get the most yeild for the lowest cost.

1 - Swiss grow show demonstrates attention to detail and exacting plant environment. This crop of White Widow is perfect! Note how the lighting is consistent and clones are all the same height and size. This grower reaped one gram per watt of light during eight weeks of flowering in this garden.

2 - Fans mounted near the ceiling circulate and help mix warm and cool air in this grow room. Perched in the foothills of the Swiss Alps, outdoor temperatures seldom climb above 70 degrees F. The grower uses heat generated by HIDs to heat the room.

3 - Peter from the Cannabis College in Amsterdam inspects a bud in the display garden. He is using a 30X magnifier to check resin glands for peak ripeness.

4 - Buds are so heavy that they must be tied up with dental floss. I am always amazed how strong and healthy plants are at the Cannabis College display garden.

POTSENALITIES

1 - We all call him Napoleon. Clutching his famous electric bud-trimming scissors, Napoleon strikes a pose in front of his image on the cover of Newsweek magazine. You can see Napoleon at all the European cannabis shows, HIGH TIMES' Cannabis Cup, the Dutch Highlife Cup, German Cannabusiness and the Swiss CannaTrade shows.

2 - Marc Emery, the Prince of Pot, marijuana activist, seed mogul and publisher of *Cannabis Culture* magazine (www.cannabisculture.com) just made and smoked a bit of screened hash at a friend's house. His smile says it all!

3 - Eagle Bill is a fixture in Amsterdam. You see him here turning a friend on to a vaporizer hit of great weed. When vaporized at 180 degrees C, cannabinoids turn into a vapor you can inhale that gets you high without the carbon and tar-packed smoke caused by burning marijuana foliage.

4 - Felipe Borallo, one of the best-known activists in Spain, takes a toke of local produce from behind his desk at Makoki Bookstore located in the heart of the Gothic Quarter in Barcelona.

5 - The Crystalman at the High Life Hemp Expo in Utrecht, Holland 2003. 3-D Glasses were offered to "enhance" the viewing experience of his awesome microphotography and the paintings he has made of Cannabis crystals. Contact the Crystalman at www.crystalman.nl

Super Size Secret:

A brix meter measures foliage sugar content, which estimates the effectiveness of fertilizers. Brix level is the key to plant health and a big harvest.

Dear Ja Swan,

The best soil mix is a subjective and depends on what there is at hand. It should retain water and air as well as allow good drainage. I like a soil or soilless mix that drains well and needs to be watered daily. Most importantly indoor soil should be used only once and then tossed out. All components of indoor soil should be sterilized. Most store-bought components are clean and free of insects, eggs and disease. Avoid backyard soil and compost. Myself, personally, I like a simple mix of coco coir (50 percent), perlite (20 percent), store-bought compost (20 percent) and worm castings (10 percent). If available, mushroom compost is an excellent choice and can constitute up to 50 percent of the mix, replacing a portion of coco coir. When purchasing coco coir, make sure all salts and other impurities have been washed out.

The best fertilizer is also subjective. Look for a high quality hydroponic soluble fertilizer, either organic or chemical-based, that is popular in your area. Start using it and stay with it. Most importantly, learn how to use it and become proficient with it. Changing fertilizers every crop or every other crop will cause you more problems than it will solve. Go to a hydroponic store where you feel comfortable, discuss your needs with the sales person. They will know much more about the local water and the best fertilizer to use with it.

Very high yielding varieties include but are not limited to: Chronic (Serious Seeds), Northern Lights (Sensi Seeds), Power Plant (Dutch Passion), Blueberry (DJ Short) and Big Bud (Sensi Seeds). When choosing a high yielding variety, always look at the time it takes to mature. For example a variety that takes 7 weeks (49 days) will yield 7 crops a year while a variety that is ready to harvest in 8 weeks (56 days) will yield 6 crops a year. If the 7-week crop yields one kilo (2.2 pounds) per 1000 watts of light during flowering (7 x 2.2 = 15.4 pounds a year) and the 8-week crop yields 1.1 kilos (2.4 pounds) per 1000 watts of light during flowering (6 x 2.4 = 14.4 pounds a year), the variety that produces more crops per year is most productive.

Cannabis Clue:

Leach soil with 1 - 2 gallons of mild nutrient solution per gallon of soil every 1 - 2 months. This is the best form of preventative maintenance against toxic salt buildup in the soil.

Super Size Secret:
Always use high quality (food grade) hydroponic nutrient components.
Low-grade components are packed with impurities.

FERTILIZER

 Dear Jorge,
I am growing with a 400 watt HPS and an ebb and flow hydroponic system. I am reading *Closet Cultivator*. The book suggests using Peters 20-20-20, but it doesn't say how much to use per gallon, so I guessed. My plants are dying, one has already died. How much should I use for a 7-gallon reservoir? How many times a day should I water? Also, I plan on moving operations to the attic. With all other measurements considered I would have 5'10" to grow. Is it enough?

Thank-you.
Chi, Cyberspace

Dear Chi,
I always recommend that people follow the manufacturer's recommendations. But, Peters 20-20-20 is a poor choice for your hydroponic setup. Find a quality hydroponic nutrient such as General, Genesis, DNF, etc., and follow the directions on the label. If you need more help with the dose, talk to the person you bought the fertilizer from or call the manufacturer. You have lots of room to grow in the attic. If the roof is insulated the tem-

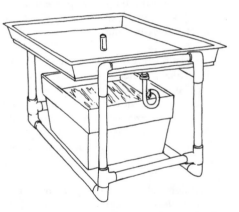

Flood and drain also called "ebb and flow" gardens pump water into a tray full of plants before draining back into the reservoir..

perature will stay cooler and more constant. Record the maximum and minimum temperatures in the attic a few days before moving. You may find you need to employ more ventilation to keep the room cool.

 Warning:
Never let the nutrient solution temperature climb above 85 degrees. Hot roots attract fatal pests and diseases and diminish oxygen uptake severely.

A **Chelate** (the Greek word for claw) is an organic molecule that forms a claw-like bond with free electrically charged "metal particles." This property keeps metal ions, such as zinc, iron, manganese, etc., soluble in water and the chelated metal's reactions with other materials is suppressed. Roots take in chelated metals in a stable soluble form that are used immediately.

HYDROPONICS

HYDRO OR SOIL?

Dear Jorge,

I see a lot for hydroponic books in HIGH TIMES. Is hydroponic better than regular soil-grown dope? Is it worth the trouble and all the special equipment necessary to grow it?

Newbie, Tennessee

Dear Newbie,

You have raised an excellent question! The response depends upon the criteria by which you judge the end result. If you are interested in smooth sweet smoke and have the hankering to keep in tune with Mother Nature, then grow only in organic soil and use naturally occurring and organic fertilizers. If simplicity, economics and control top your criteria, then buy inexpensive grow bags and fill them with soilless mix and feed with a quality hydroponic fertilizer. If you are into exacting control, technical stuff, gadgets, cleanliness and spending money, buy an expensive hydroponic system.

Now here is the fun part. With a little homework, experience and hard work, both soil and hydroponic gardens will yield similar amounts for the average home grower over the long haul. Light is the most common limiting factor to overall yield. If yield is your criteria, gain as much experience as possible growing all types of plants. Use every lumen of light to its fullest potential and never let the grow room sit fallow. Follow these simple guidelines and you will always have enough smoke to share with friends.

TAKE IT SLOW

Jorge,

The leaves on my plants have brown blotches and curl downward. The tips are yellow and burnt. The plants are 12 inches tall and light green. I grow in a NFT system. The pH is 6 and EC 1.25. I have changed nutrients in the reservoir and added Superthrive. I sprayed with a 2 percent solution of Epsom salts today. Please help!

Bazza, Newport Beach, CA

Dear Bazza,

My guess is that you have very little experience growing indoors and that this is your first time growing in an NFT system. The plants have probably been receiving an imbalanced nutrient regimen since the day they were placed in the system, and the overt signs of the imbalance did not manifest until they were a foot tall. This is a very standard scenario. NFT systems are incredibly productive when conditions are perfect. When one small thing is off, the entire system becomes unproductive fast.

EC (electrical conductivity) is a measure of the entire strength of the nutrient solution, including the input water. If your input water has a high level of sodium or a menagerie of other common tap water pollutants, it will raise the EC and distort the balance of pre-mixed nutrients. Relatively low levels of sodium (50 PPM) and higher levels of other nutrients will block most nutrients from entering plant roots, actually causing dehydration and leaves to curl downward. EC does not measure the strength of each individual nutrient or the relationship between nutrients. Consequently, all the nitrogen, for example, could be used quickly and the EC would lower slightly, but the only nutrient missing would be nitrogen. If you "top off" the nutrient solution with new nutrient solution, you will still have a proportionately lower level of nitrogen. Changing the nutrient solution often does not always solve the nutrient deficiency because it does not provide proportionately more of the deficient nutrient. Nor does it change the possible characteristics of the system that could have caused the deficiency in the first place.

Often NFT systems are poorly designed or poorly managed. If the inside of the gullies are too hot or cold, or if nutrient flows inconsistently over roots, or if they receive light inside, all kinds of weird things could happen that will cause the above reactions to your plants.

Here is my advice, buy a copy of the book *ABC of NFT*, by Dr. Alan Cooper. Read it cover to cover. Then decide if you want to continue to grow with a NFT system. Meantime, pick up some soil or soilless mix and three-gallon pots. Take a new batch of clones and grow them out in the soilless mix. Water with the same nutrient solution you are using now. Alongside of this easy-to-manage garden, grow a crop in the NFT system and see which one is more productive. Follow this advice and you will be in smoke forever!

HYDRO OR AERO?

Dear Jorge,
I want to start growing the best marijuana possible. I have experimented with soil-grown marijuana and want to try hydroponics or aeroponics. But I heard aeroponic bud was not as good as hydro. Aeroponic systems can deliver nutrients with up to 99 percent effectiveness compared to hydro's 80 percent. Which is better?

Crazy Tom, Texas

Dear Crazy Tom,

Aeroponic systems mist roots suspended in air.

Do you get your information from advertisements and grower friends who have never shown you their garden? Most growers do. Marijuana potency is determined by genetics, not aeroponics or hydroponics. Do your plants yield 0.5 grams per watt every 30 days of flowering? One half GPW/30 means each 1000w light in the flowering room produces just over a pound (500 grams) of dry manicured bud every 30 days. If you are achieving these yields, in soil or hydroponics, you can still do better, and you do not need fancy grow systems. All you need is grow-how, skill. If your goal is to spend a lot of money and time entertaining yourself with a hobby, get into aeroponics. If your goal is to grow high-quality bud for a few bucks, start with good genetics (seeds or clones, 'Chronic' is outstanding), give them plenty of light, grow in a soilless medium, use high quality hydroponic fertilizer, avoid nutrient problems by watering heavily and letting excess drain out bottom of containers. Keep temperature at 75 degrees (day) and 60-65 (night), humidity about 50 percent and keep the room clean to prevent insects and diseases. Keep each and every plant growing fast and strong at all times. Grow more plants than you plan to harvest. Remove weak sickly plants. Master these simple principles, choose good genetics, and your harvest will top out at 1 GPW/30!

A wick system is simple and low maintenance. The wick carries nutrient solution up to the roots.

BUILD YOUR OWN SYSTEM

LONDON GROW KIT

 Hello.

I have recently moved from South Africa to London where cannabis is not as available or as cheap. How do I go about getting a growing kit and high-quality seeds to grow? Also is there a way of ordering nice buds and is it safe to have them shipped to me in London or do I need to travel to get what I want?

Help! Help!

Thanks

AntAcid, London

Designer grow closets became popular at the turn of the century. The 'plug and play' grow shows are a perfect solution to many growers problems.

Dear AntAcid,

Glad to hear marijuana is readily available and economical in South Africa. Hash is the most popular form of cannabis in the United Kingdom. Watch out for low quality "soap" hash. Seeds are legal to sell in the UK and available in many retail locations. They are also available in the Netherlands. Call WEED WORLD magazine, +44-(0) 1974-821-518, to subscribe to the magazine. It is packed with information and lots of seed company ads.

Look up "hydroponics" in the local telephone directory to find a supplier in your area. You can also call one of the biggest manufacturers of hydroponic gear on the islands, Growth Technology, +44 (1) 823-325-291 for the location of a shop near you.

Do it Yourself

Jorge,

Could you supply me with people who have web sites that can help me build my own hydro system?

Many thanks,

Johno, Internet

Dear Johno,

One of my favorite sites is www.overgrow.com. They have plans for a bubbler hydroponic garden. It is the subject of lots of posts in the chat group. You will have countless growers that have hands-on experience with this garden to help you through each step. They also have accurate construction photos, lists of construction materials, and photos of gardens. At first I was not sold on this garden because I thought the yield was low for the amount of work involved. However, after watching the bubbler gardens grow on the Internet for some time, I have changed my beliefs about the bubbler garden. I give my sincere thanks to all the growers who post in the chat room and the guys from www.overgrow.com for helping me change!

Hydroponics Tip:
Pruning off all lower branches makes inspecting irrigation fittings easy and diminishes problems with weak growth.

Air

Too Much Hot Air?

Jorge,

Should I cycle ventilation or should I keep the fan running all the time? I use a bathroom exhaust fan to vent odors and circulate air. If I add CO_2, should I turn it off or leave it on? Air is important to my darlings and me. Please help.

Thank you,

Daddy in Cyberspace

Dear Daddy,

Circulation and ventilation, although invisible are often the source of more problems than any other grow room necessity. Circulating air in the grow room keeps it from stratifying (hot on top and cold on the bottom) and also forces new CO_2-rich air around foliage. Use an oscillating circulation fan in the room to keep the air stirred up. Relying on an extraction (vent) fan will not be enough. Ventilation is of utmost importance because it removes hot, humid, CO_2-depleted air. Ideally you should keep the air temperature about 75 degrees during the day and no lower than 60 degrees at night. Relative humidity should stay about 50 percent. There are a multitude of reasons for these parameters that I will not discuss now. Just know your darlings will love it. If you must keep the vent fan on 24 hours a day or vent sporadically to achieve this environment, then that's the answer.

You will need an accurate thermometer and hygrometer to measure temperature and humidity. One note of caution, when you measure relative humidity, make sure to measure and record it several times during the day and night. When the lights go out at night, the temperature drops a few degrees. This is when the humidity can climb quickly. For example, this problem plagued Sensi Seeds breeding facility. A computer-controlled interface measures and plots air temperature and humidity in their high-tech grow rooms. Upon examining printouts of temperature and humidity levels, I noticed that humidity levels spike up for 30 minutes to an hour after the lights are turned off. But, the ventilation fans are unable to evacuate the moist air in less than an hour. Some of the rooms experienced humidity-related problems caused by the increase. Your darlings may have the same problem.

CO_2 enhanced environments require vigorous air circulation and an integrated ventilation regimen. If injecting bottled CO_2 into a small room, vent the room as per manufacturer's instructions. The temperature can run up to 85 degrees safely and humidity can climb to 60 percent.

HOT WATER!

Dear Jorge,

I have 10 plants in a 4-tray Aero-Jet hydroponic system in a 10 x 10 room. The plants are in the last weeks of flowering. They are lit for 12 hours daily by a 400w HP sodium on a Light Rail. CO_2 is supplemented at 1000 PPM, air circulation and ventilation are good. The room temperature room fluctuates from 78 to 88 degrees F. I'm using Botanicare and Cal-mag at as per label instructions, 1100 PPM. The pH is 6.4. I have changed water three times since starting. My plants are a nice jade green but the largest upper leaves are very wrinkled and feel dry and have been this way since plants were 10 inches tall during vegetative growth. They are producing nice 'Skunk #6' buds but the plant looks so unhealthy. Please help! You are my last hope.

Sincerely,
Very Frustrated in cyberspace

Dear Frustrated,

There are several things going on that make the leaves wrinkled and dry. The problem appears to be a lack of phosphorous and potassium. Without seeing the plants and playing in your grow room a bit, it is difficult to tell for sure. Look for these symptoms and answer the following questions to find out.

A deficiency of phosphorous causes stunted growth. Leaves are smaller, bluish-green or jade colored and often with blotches. Stems, leaf stems (petioles) and main veins often but not always turn reddish-purple starting on leaf underside. Leaf tips of older leaves turn dark and curl downward. If severe, large purplish-black dead blotches develop, later entire leaves turn bronzish-purple, dry, shrivel up, contort and fall off. Flowering is slow and buds are smaller and susceptible to disease. The condition is aggravated when the root zone is very wet and the oxygen content is low. Deficiencies are more common when there is an excess of phosphates, iron and zinc.

Potassium deficient plants look healthy at first, but later older leaves, first tips and margins, followed by whole leaves turn dark yellow and die. Stems are often weak and sometimes brittle. Potassium is usually present, but locked in by high salinity. The deficiency causes the temperature inside leaves to climb, frying protein cells. This is what makes leaves dry and brittle. They evaporate off moisture to cool down. The evaporation is highest on leaf margins where the burns appear first.

The reasons for all the problems are straightforward and come from one simple source, the room is too hot. Even though plants can take more heat and process the extra CO_2 when the temperature is up to 90 degrees F, the roots cannot. The nutrient solution will be at least as warm as the ambient air temperature, often times hotter! The nutrient solution can hold much less oxygen when at 90 degrees than it can when it is held at 60 degrees. This is why sea life abounds in cold waters, oxygen. Roots need oxygen to be able to absorb nutrients via osmosis. In a low-oxygen atmosphere, nutrient uptake is severely limited and deficiencies occur quickly regardless of the strength of the nutrient solution. Deficiencies started to manifest in older leaves when plants were about 6 weeks old and plants 10 inches tall. This means the deficiencies started soon after plants were moved into the system. The nutrient solution is trapped inside a chamber. The light falls on the chamber, further heating the solution to beyond 90 degrees. It could easily reach more than 100 degrees F around the root zone!

Also check the roots for signs of rot and disease. They should be a healthy robust white with plenty of tiny hair-like feeder roots growing from main roots. Roots that are brown and rotten are sure signs their environment is too hot.

You can cool the nutrient solution with a reservoir chiller found at hydroponic stores. The chillers can be cumbersome and expensive if you have to chill much hot water to 60 degrees F or less. Your best bet is to remove the CO_2, lower the room temperature to 70- 75 degrees F during the day and to below 60 degrees F at night. This will keep the nutrient solution cooler and expedite proper nutrient uptake. It is also easier and less expensive to cool water from 70 down to 60 degrees F.

Other things that make the problems worse include pH and nutrient solution concentration. Running the pH at 5.8 to 6.0 will increase nutrient absorption. Changing the nutrient solution once a week will help keep the nutrients balanced. Remember that plants use much more water than nutrients, especially when the temperatures are higher. The water evaporates (transpires) off to cool leaves and nutrient solution concentrates. You should "top off" the nutrient solution with plain water to replenish the water evaporated into the air.

CO_2

CO_2 AND GOOD SHIT

Hi Jorge.

First, thank you for being there.

I am a beginner indoor grower. This is my second harvest. Although experience comes with practice over years, I have done good work until now. I have three, 3-foot-tall ladies under a 400w HP sodium. This is their third week of flowering. I fertilize them with Peters 10-30-20 once every second watering using half dosage.

It is difficult for me to get a tank of CO_2. Can I use the small CO_2 cylinders found in air guns? I have my plants in a mix 2:1 of compost, perlite and want to stop using Peters and switch to an organic nutrient tea mix. Do you have a recipe?

Thanks,

DAGGA BOY, Peru, NY

Dear Dagga,

The CO_2 cylinders found in air rifles and pistols are punctured and sealed. When the gun needs more air to launch a projectile, it is quickly metered out of the cylinder. If you were to open one of these cylinders, chances are the entire amount of CO_2 would escape at once. First make sure that everything in the garden is running at maximum capacity before adding CO_2. Make CO_2 in the room inexpensively by burning a petroleum product – kerosene, natural gas, propane, etc. If an open flame is unappealing, make CO_2 by mixing baking soda with vinegar. Meter the vinegar (acetic acid) one drop at a time into a bed of baking soda. The exact amount of CO_2 is difficult to determine and the levels will fluctuate, but the method is inexpensive.

Cannabis Clue:

On the average, a 5-pound block of dry ice will last about 24 hours.

If CO_2 increases yield by 25 percent, then you would have the same effect by adding one more plant to the garden. Increasing the yield by doubling the number of plants from three to six would also be a very inexpensive alternative to CO_2.

Three soluble organic fertilizers you can't beat are fish emulsion, bat guano and seaweed. A good recipe is to use fish emulsion for vegetative growth and switch to bat guano during flowering. Add seaweed with each watering. Norwegian kelp is one of the best sources for micronutrients and lots of other good stuff. Excellent organic fertilizers include Fox Farms, Earth Juice and Pure Blend.

DRY ICE

Dear Jorge,

A friend told me about dry ice. He said he put 4 or 5 pieces around plants when they are 2.5 inches tall and they will grow better. Does this do any good or is it a waste of time?

Crossbone, Lodi, CA

Dear Crossbone,

Dry ice releases carbon dioxide (CO_2) as it melts which is beneficial to plants, which can use more CO_2 than the amount (350 PPM) that occurs naturally in the atmosphere. But, securing enough dry ice to melt down every day is very expensive and much more trouble than it is worth. Spend your time nurturing plants. The investment in learning how to grow well will be paid back many times over.

Put dry ice in a plastic container with holes to slow evaporation of CO_2 gas.

ODOR

CHARCOAL FILTERS

Hey Jorge,

Can you send me information on charcoal filters? I grow in an apartment.

Thanks,

Anonymous, Florida Panhandle

Dear Anonymous,

Charcoal filters are fantastic and they work! The activated charcoal absorbs the odor molecules. The mechanics are simple and there are only three things to remember when using a charcoal filter: 1. Keep room humidity about 50 percent. At about 65-70 percent humidity, the charcoal absorbs moisture and clogs. At 80 percent humidity it stops removing odors. 2. Air must move slowly through charcoal filter to extract odors.

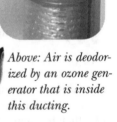

Above: Air is deodorized by an ozone generator that is inside this ducting.

Left: After passing through an ozone chamber for one minute air is fresh and clean.

Above: A vent fan duct hooks to each tube and the air-cleansing agent is imparted before air is evacuated.

The fan on professional units let just enough air through the filter so the odors have enough (dwell) time to be absorbed by the carbon filter. 3. Use a pre-filter. The pre-filter catches most of the dust and airborne pollutants before they foul the carbon filter. Change the pre-filter regularly, every 60 days, more often if the room is dusty. Carbon lasts about a year. Many growers prefer coconut carbon.

STINKY SMOKE

Dear Jorge,

I'm growing in a 10 x 10 area in a very private, secure space. How can I control the odor? Fans help with the air exchange, but the heat and smell are getting out of control.

Party naked in the Puget Sound!

Mr. Peabody, Seattle, WA

Dear Mr. Peabody.,

Hot rooms smell more than temperate ones. Keeping the room no warmer than 75 degrees F will reduce fragrant odors, but it will not abate them completely. If your entire crop comes ripe at once, the last two to four weeks really reek, depending upon the variety. Unfortunately, the most fragrant marijuana is often the most potent. You may need to add more ventilation to your room. The easiest ways to increase expelled airflow include revamping your exhaust system so that air does not have to turn corners and the fan should be as close to the outlet as possible. This will ensure the fan is operating efficiently. I also suggest an ozone generator to control unwanted odors. There are many brands on the market from which to choose. Remember to follow manufacturer's instructions to the letter to get the most efficient use of the ozone generator.

OZONE AT NIGHT?

Dear Jorge,

I purchased a "Silver Bullet" ozone generator. Is it OK to leave it on at night? I'm in the flowering stage now, and the ozone generator emits a bluish UV light at night. Will this light keep my plants from blooming?

T-BONE
Northern Florida

Dear T-BONE,

Plants emit odors at night too. Set the timer so it comes on intermittently before venting the room at night. The blue UV light should cause little problem as long as it does not shine on plants. Block plants from UV light with a simple plastic or cardboard partition.

PESTS
MITES FOREVER!

Dear Dr. Jorge,

I have been growing organically for about five years. I have always had problems with pests but nothing that ladybugs couldn't handle. A few months ago I got some clones of 'Juicy Fruit.' Ever since then I have had problems with spider mites. I can't seem to eradicate this problem and until I do my life and my garden are in limbo. Please help!!... What can I do?

Sincerely,

Supershiva
Calgary, Canada

Dear Supershiva,

Spider mites have ruined more than one growers' night's sleep! This is after the fact, but you should have quarantined the plants before introducing them into the garden. Always dip the entire plant, pot and all, in a miticide solution – pyrethrum and or neem oil. Dip the plant at least twice at three-day intervals. Carefully inspect new plants to ensure there are no eggs or mites.

To rid your garden of mites, you will have to clean everything. If possible, after harvest, remove all plants from the grow room. Scrub the entire room down with a 5 percent bleach solution. You might even want to set off a bug bomb, available at most hydroponic stores and many discount stores. Next, dip all plants in a miticide solution - follow directions above. Once plants are in the garden again, smear Tanglefoot™ around the rim of each container and the base of all plants. This will hinder mite's migration from one plant to another. Spray plants individually with pyrethrum in an aerosol form. Tip the plants to the side and spray under the leaves where mites and eggs reside. Spray plants a minimum of four times at 5-day intervals. Sleep well!

Warning:
Do not use Systemic products!

WHITEFLIES!

Dear Jorge,

When I moved my plants I discovered I have whiteflies. I've been using Volck Oil Spray but it doesn't seem to be working. Bug-B-Gone doesn't work ether. The leaves are brown and slimy. I'm at a loss, please help!

Major Tom, Cyberspace

Dear Major Tom,

Check for whiteflies by shaking branches. Winged adults will flutter up from leaf undersides. This means you have an infestation! The small white, moth-like insects are a scant millimeter long. They appear near the tops of weak plants first.

Spray with insecticidal soap or pyrethrum (aerosol) for rapid results. Apply yellow sticky traps near colonies to monitor populations perpetually.

Brown slimy leaves probably means you have other serious problems, probably a fungus or disease. Remove severely damaged leaves from plants and grow room. Wash hands with soap and water before touching, and possibly re-infecting, foliage. Whiteflies and other insects often vector (transmit) diseases.

Logical Progression of Insect Control:

1. Prevention
   a. cleanliness
   b. use "new" soil
   c. one "indoor" set of tools
   d. disease-resistant plants
   e. healthy plants
   f. climate control
   g. no animals
   h. companion planting

2. Manual Removal
   a. fingers
   b. sponges

3. Organic Sprays

4. Natural Predators

5. Chemicals

Super Size Secret:

Preventing pests and diseases is much easier and more productive than eliminating an infestation.

STINKY SOIL AND GNATS

I am growing in organic soil with vermiculite, perlite, blood meal and bone meal added. I like the mix but it stinks and attracts fungus gnats. Malathion kills the gnats but will not touch the whiteflies. I used Safer's® Insecticidal soap on the whiteflies and it worked, but the gnats came back. Is there bone meal and blood meal that does not stink? How do I control gnats and whiteflies?

Thanks,
Closet Cloner, San Jose, CA

Dear Closet Cloner,

I find it weird that you spend the time and energy to grow organically and use Malathion, which is known to cause cancer! Take that bottle of poison and hand it over to the hazardous materials guys at the landfill and do not use it in your garden again. Even though the bottle says it's approved as a contact spray for edibles, it stays on plants much longer indoors and could prove harmful.

Fungus gnats need a moist environment to live and they thrive on rotting vegetative matter. Your soil probably stays too wet and roots could be rotting too. This is a perfect environment for them to live. Remove the vermiculite from your mix to improve drainage. If gnats persist, use natural Bacillus thuringiensis var. israelensis (Bti) sold under the brand names Vectobac®, Gnatrol® or Bactimos®. Continue using Safer's® Insecticidal soap on whiteflies. Add an oscillating circulation fan that keeps leaves on all plants fluttering to further discourage whiteflies. You may be able to find deodorized blood meal. Bone meal should not smell bad if it is steamed rather than raw. I suggest that you substitute alfalfa meal for the nitrogen source and stop using blood meal.

TOXIC PESTICIDE!

Jorge,

My plants had some bugs on them so I sprayed them with some Ortho Houseplant and Garden Insect Killer. I later noticed in small print to use only on "NON-EDIBLE" plants. Did I screw up my plant? Was that small amount really harmful?

Dwane from NY

Poor Dwane,

What a bummer. That toxic stuff is for ORNAMENTALS ONLY! The reason it is not for consumable plants is because it is systemic. Systemic sprays actually penetrate and flow in the fluids of a plant, carrying poison throughout. This poison is now in the plant's system and will take several months to dissipate.

Paraquat, the chemical used to spray Mexican marijuana fields is also a systemic spray, and a known carcinogen. Hundreds of thousands of stoners toked up on the Paraquat-tainted Mexican.

I would not smoke the stuff.

SOME KILLER TIPS

Howdee,

Here are some tried-and-true tips for y'all.

1. To get rid of mites, try buttermilk! Use 1/4 cup buttermilk, 4 cups of wheat flour and 5 gallons of water. Strain and spray infected plants. This kills mites and their eggs.

2. This recipe was developed to extend the life of cut flowers, but it works great to root cuttings. Try dipping clones in a mix of 3 large capfuls of Listerine mouthwash to 1.5 gallons water. Listerine contains sucrose (food for plants), a bactericide and its acidity helps promote quicker uptake of water by the plants.

3. Yellow index cards coated with petroleum jelly helps trap whiteflies, aphids and a buncha other common insects.

Hope these tips help someone, they sure helped me!!

Sabuddha Howasaki
Cleveland, OH

Dear Sabuddha,

Your tips remind me of Jerry Baker's Gardening for Life www.jerrybaker.com. You can find all kinds of off-the-wall tips and tonics on his site. Check out his site to see where he applies beer and baby shampoo in the garden!

Rule of Thumb:

To control a fungus, it should be identified so that a specific fungicide can be applied.

DISEASES

FEEBLE FEMALES, MOLDY NUGS

Dear Jorge,

I have been growing clones from the same strain for about 20 generations. The quality is good, but the buds are very small and stringy. My room is 11 x 12 and I use a 1000w HID. I grow them for 3 to 4 months before switching them a 12/12 flowering cycle. The budding process takes more than 12 weeks. The room is vented and I use General Hydroponics as per instructions. How far away should the light source be? I do not use my 400w HPS because I haven't noticed any difference. Do you have any good tips for drying and curing? I keep losing bud to mold when drying.

KDS, Cyberspace

Dear KDS,

Small stringy buds come from wispy weak plants. You are growing plants too long before switching them to the 12/12 day/night photoperiod. If the plants grow 12 inches a month, they are 3 to 4 feet tall before flowering is induced. Tops elongate at least 12 inches during flowering. Plants will be 4 to 5 feet tall at harvest. That's too tall. HID light looses intensity exponentially fast (Intensity = light output/distance squared). A 1000w metal halide produces 100,000 lumens at its source. Two feet away, at the canopy of the garden, there are only 25, 000 lumens. Four feet away 12,500 lumens and 6 feet away, near the bottom of the plant, there are only 8,333 lumens. This example does not take into account an efficient reflective hood. Weak light causes plants to develop feebly and flower slowly. A plant that normally flowers in 8 weeks could take more than 10 weeks to develop completely.

Clones taken from flowering plants and re-vegetated are not as strong, produce poorly and are prone to sickness. The end product of such clones is diminished when mothers are weak. Adding another small light to stimulate extra growth in such plants will do little good.

Section off a 4 x 4 room and illuminate it with the 400w HPS. Grow mothers and clones in this room under 18 hours of light. Take clones from mothers in this room and root them under fluorescent light. Once well rooted, and 6 to 12 inches high, move them into the flowering room and keep the 1000w HID about 24 inches above.

Ventilation and air circulation are also a factor. The air in the room should change at least once every hour to ensure adequate carbon dioxide is available and to control heat and keep humidity under 50 percent. Have you taken a burning joint or smoke stick and held it near the bottom of plants to see if the smoke moves quickly up and out the vent? Add oscillating circulating fans everywhere air movement is slow. Ideally all leaves on all plants should flutter slightly.

My best guess is that living plants have fungus before they are dry. The most common fungal disease is *Botrytis cinera*, commonly called gray mold. Botrytis usually starts inside buds and is difficult to see the grayish, whitish to bluish-green in color. Botrytis appears hair-like, similar to laundry lint, in moist climates. As the disease progresses foliage turns somewhat slimy. Damage can also appear as dark brownish spots on buds in less humid environments. Dry to the touch, *Botrytis* affected area often crumbles if rubbed. Gray mold attacks countless other crops and airborne spores are present virtually everywhere. While most commonly found attacking dense, swelling flower buds, it also attacks stems, leaves, seeds, causes damping-off and decomposes dry stored bud.

Also transmitted via seeds.

The plants are living too long and poor cultural practices make them prone to disease. Plants probably have spider mites, which predisposes them further to fungal disease.

Remove dead leaves including stems (petioles) from stalks, which often harbor *Botrytis*. Keep the grow room clean!! Use fresh sterile growing medium for each crop.

Inspect regularly for mold. Use alcohol-sterilized pruners to remove *Botrytis*-infected buds/foliage at least one inch below the infected area. Do not let the bud or anything that touched it contaminate foliage. Remove from the garden and destroy. Wash your hands and tools after removing. Excessive nitrogen and phosphorus levels make foliage tender so Botrytis can get a foothold. Keep pH to around 6 to facilitate calcium uptake. Botrytis needs UV light to complete its life cycle. Exclude all light when drying. If changing cultural practices fails to arrest botrytis, spray plants with *Gliocladium roseum* and *Trichoderma* species.

Logical Progression of Fungus Control

Prevention
   a) cleanliness
   b) low humidity
   c) ventilation
Removal
Copper, lime sulfur sprays
Specific fungicide

Rule of Thumb:

To control a fungus, it should be identified so that a specific fungicide can be applied.

POWDERY MILDEW

Hi Jorge,

Is there any way to prevent powdery mildew completely from growing on your plants besides using sulfur?

Guerilla Grower, Austin, Texas

Dear G.G.,

Sulfur functions as a fungistat, arresting surface development, not as a fungicide, which kills the disease inside the plant. The first indication of powdery mildew infection is small sores (spots) on the top of leaves. Spots progress to a fine pale gray/white powdery coating on growing shoots, leaves and stems. Powdery mildew is limited to the upper surface of foliage. Growth slows, leaves yellow and plants die as the disease advances. Fatal if allowed to progress, this disease is at its worst when roots dry out and foliage is moist. Plants are infected for weeks before they show the first symptoms.

Prevent this mildew by avoiding cool, damp, humid, dim areas. Low light levels and stale air mitigate this disease. Remove and destroy foliage more than 50 percent infected and avoid excess nitrogen.

If the condition is out of hand, apply Serenade® (*Bacillus subtilis*) or spray with a saturation mix of baking soda and water. Bordeaux mixture (copper and sulfur) may keep this mold in check. A saturation baking soda spray dries to a fine powder on leaf. The baking soda changes the surface pH of the leaf to 7 and powdery mildew cannot grow.

Super Size Secret:

Always plant about 10 percent more plants than you plan to havest. If one in 10 plants becomes infected or sickly, remove them from the garden. Removing entire plants is the easiest way to isolate and control most pest and disease problems.

Cannabis Clue:

Maintain the growing medium temperature between 75 - 80 degrees F.
day and night to root cuttings fast.

Seeds and Seedlings

Safety in Numbers

Hello Jorge,

We just started growing our first cannabis plant. How much water
should we give it per week? Is the sun in England bright enough to make it
bud if it is on the windowsill? Should we buy a light?

Cheers,

Lorne and Steve, Portsmouth, UK

Dear Lorne and Steve,

Increase your odds of growing a female by planting a few more
plants. Likelihood of your single plant turning out to be a female is 50/50.
You should grow a minimum of 3 plants to increase provability of at least one
being female. I suggest you grow more especially if starting from seed. Grow a
minimum of two if starting female clones. Much can happen to a single plant
before harvest, including fatal disease and pest attacks, poor cultural practices
and accidents. What if the single plant is inadvertently bumped and falls to
the floor and the stem is severed?

Water plants less than a foot tall when the surface is dry. Taller plants
should receive water when growing medium is dry one half-inch from the top.
Frequency depends upon climatic conditions, plant growth rate, consistency
of growing medium, and container size. Check soil moisture daily. Lightly cultivate soil surface so water penetrates evenly. Shield container from heating
sunlight to avoid cooking roots. Make sure 10-25 percent of the irrigation
water drains from the bottom of the container upon each watering.

Super Size Secret:

If you want to harvest 3 females, plant 10 seeds. Five could be
male, two can be thinned and three to harvest.

This year has been rainier than normal in the UK. Clouds regularly blanket the British Isles, and port towns see even more rain and clouds. Buy a 150-400w High Intensity Discharge (HP sodium or metal halide) lamp. Find a hydroponic store in the local or national Yellow Pages and spend time at the store talking to patrons and salespeople so you get the feel of growing in your area. Also pick up a good grow book for more detailed instructions.

SLOW SEEDLING

Dear Jorge

The cotyledon leaves on my two-week-old seedlings have turned yellow. They are growing under two fluorescent lights in a Grow Cube. They were just moved to a larger container. What should I do to help my plants out? I am using a Shultz Potting Soil Plus with perlite. I haven't used any supplements. I fertilize with Miracle Grow (15-30-15).

Later,
Guy from Texas

Dear Guy,

You may be killing your seedlings with kindness. The Grow Cube has little air circulation, which means the soil stays wet longer. Low light levels keep plants growing slowly and they become more susceptible to environmental forces. Seedlings are prone to several fungal diseases including pythium, fusarium and verticillium wilts. These diseases are referred to as "damping off" and cause seedlings to rot at the soil line. Symptoms of damping off often include a tall spindly stem and premature yellow leaves. My guess is that the soil is too moist and damping off has set in. There is only one cure for damping off, remove all affected plants and soil. Install new soil and start over. Watch the soil moisture carefully. Take the lid off the Grow Cube to allow more air ventilation and circulation. This time, apply fertilizer quarter strength when plants are three weeks old.

GROWING FEMALE SEEDLINGS

Jorge,

How do I tell the difference between the male and female seeds? What fertilizer do I use to make plants more potent? How long does it take for a plant to grow from seed to harvest? How long do buds take to dry?

M. P. S., Brooklyn, NY

Dear M.,

Distinguishing between male and female seeds is impossible. However, you can tip the scales in your favor. Controlling the environment is the key. Once seedlings have three pairs of true leaves (not counting cotyledons) environmental factors will influence sex determination.

To increase the provability of seeds growing into female plants: increase the level of nitrogen and lower the level of potassium in the seedbed during the first two weeks after planting. Keep the seedbed temperature low, below 75 degrees F. Retain high humidity, above 70 percent. Keep the seedbed moist but not soggy enough to foster damping off. Increase the amount of blue light in the spectrum. Keep the light on for 14 hours per day during the first two or three weeks of growth. Reduce stress on the seedlings to a minimum.

For more information on growing seeds that turn into female plants, hit this site: http://www.dutch-passion.nl.

CLONING/MOTHERS

CLONING KLUTZ

Jorge,

I can't clone for shit. I'm wasting tons of clones, money and time. I read the books and everything. This is the only thing holding me back! Do my plants have to be 2 months old or do they have to be 2 feet high? Does the clone itself have to be 4 or 6 inches long? They say to use rooting gel. I am using Olivia's Cloning Gel. How long before they root? Seven to 10 days? I am using rockwool cubes. Can you please, please tell me the easiest way to do this? Please!

Thank you, Lenny, NY

Dear Lenny,

Remember how difficult it was to learn to ride a bicycle? Did you stop trying or did you keep working on it until you could ride with your friends? You can clone. Continue working at it until you get it down. Remember, every good grower has killed his or her fair share of plants. Once you understand what the plants need, clones will stick 100 percent.

Books are a great place to start. Here is some background and a few basics that will increase clone survival rates. First, think of what's happening when a clone is made. A stem from the mother plant is cut, half defoliated, rolled in a sticky hormone and stuck in a medium. This severed stick transforms into a plant. The stem has to draw in moisture and support the entire cutting. A smaller cutting with less foliage is better able to survive this traumatic transformation from severed stem to healthy plant.

Mother plants should be at least two months old, preferably older. Shorter 2 – 3-inch clones tend to root better. Cutting the leaves in half ensures foliage transpires (sheds water vapor) less. Pry or cut apart the rockwool cube in two with the grain and set the stem into the part block. Press the block back together so the cutting stem is in between the parted block. Keep the clones evenly moist and covered with a humidity tent under fluorescent lights. Place the humidity tent up on blocks after two days to ensure fresh air flow. Clones root best when the humidity is high and the light levels relatively low.

Growers often try to root clones too fast. Wait until you can see white fuzzy roots growing through the cubes. Transplant into larger rockwool cubes or into soil. Make sure to keep cubes well watered until roots grow into new medium.

TRANSPLANTING

TRANSPLANT SHOCK

Jorge,

I'm growing a killer 'Indica' strain but the leaves are dropping and the stems are turning red. Could it have something to do with me moving them from one part of the house to the other? I also transplanted them just before moving them and the grow room. Maybe transplanting is the problem. Either way, I gotta get these little girls to grow right.

Indica Man

Dear Indica Man,

You have several things going on. From the information you gave me, I can say that if the stems have recently turned red they probably lack potassium. However some plants genetically have red stems. Lack of potassium (K) is normally caused by excessive sodium, calcium or magnesium in your water. If you live in an arid climate and your water has a pH above 7.5, this is probably the case. The excessive levels of sodium, calcium or magnesium block the uptake of potassium. Normally it is the sodium that is the big trouble causer. Remedy this problem by leaching the soil heavily with 3 gallons of water per gallon of soil, lower pH with a product called "pH Down" to 6.5 and use only chelated potassium that is readily available.

Jorge's Rx
Super Size Secret:
Transplant entire root ball or cube into larger volume of growing medium. Expose tender roots to air and sunlight sparingly and water well to avoid transplant shock.

Leaf drop could be caused by different temperature and humidity in respective rooms. Anytime you change climate, it shocks plants. If the plants are weak or stressed from the start, leaf drop is common. Leaf drop is a way to conserve energy within the plant so that it will survive stressful conditions.

Transplanting could have also caused leaf drop. Transplanting should disturb roots as little as possible and the growing medium used should be the same. Different growing mediums cause an imbalance in hydroscopic pressure within the medium causing disproportionate water allocation to the roots. Solve transplant shock by watering with Vitamin B1, available as an additive in many products or sold separately. Or solve transplant shock by planting in biodegradable peat moss pots. To transplant, plant entire pot into a larger container full of soil.

PRUNING AND BENDING

TOPPING PLANTS

Dear Jorge,

How often should you "top" a plant? How does topping affect the total yield and time to harvest? Do you end up with the same gross yield of more but smaller buds when you top.
    If growing outdoors and time were not a factor, it seems that you would get a higher yield by topping. Also, repeated topping might help reduce detection by distorting the shape of the plant away from its usual, recognizable, cone shape. Whataya think?

Thanks,
Possum, Cyberspace

This plant was pruned to four central branches that produced four large buds.

Dear Possum,

Pruning or topping a plant refers to cutting off the growing tip(s), which forces the plant to bush out. Left alone in a flat field, most cannabis grows into a conical Christmas tree shape. Cutting the tip of the central stem forces hormones or auxins, concentrated in the growing branch tips to diffuse and concentrate in uncut tips. Pruning outdoor plants growing for more than three months does not hurt them, but does not necessarily make them produce more. Repeated topping will cause hormones to diffuse so much as to delay flower formation and harvest. In any event, topped plants produce more smaller buds.

Warning:
Pruning does not make plants produce a heavier yield.

Distorting the way plants look is a great way to camouflage them. Removing or bending plants into hedges or strange shapes works well. Also, inter-planting with other foliage that is similar in color, shape and size is very confusing to the eye.

Another alternative is to bend branches, tying them down or using wire to direct their growth. Branch buds orient toward sun and hormones are diffused less.

BONDAGE AND BUDS

Jorge,

How can I keep my outdoor plants from growing more than 3 feet tall without pruning them and delaying harvest? I'm in an area where the choppers are hell and my plants must be short and flower quickly. Is morning or afternoon sun better for outdoor plants? I would like to send photos into HIGH TIMES, but where can I get them developed safely?

Thanks,

Guerilla Grower's Union, Southeast, GA

Dear Guerilla Union Organizer,

Bending plants will keep them with a low profile and not delay harvest if plants receive at least 6 hours of full midday sun. Bend the main stem over so that it is parallel with the ground and secure it in place with tie downs. Make sure the stem is not bound tightly which will cut off fluid flow. Bend and secure each of the lateral branches with tie downs so they are parallel with the ground. Keep the branches far enough apart to allow for future growth. The day after you tie the main stem and branches down, the tips will start growing upward toward the sun. Continue tying down branches when they grow upward too far.

Sunshine is brightest during the middle of the day, from 9 AM through 4 PM. Sunshine is a bit brighter from 10 AM through 2 PM. If you had a choice between AM and PM, choose PM and the closer to noon the better.

Take photos so that no easy-to-identify landmarks or tale-tell numbers are visible. Only pot shots should appear on a roll. Do not shoot photos of friends, family, landmarks on the same roll. Take photos to a large commercial lab where processing is done mechanically and employees are unlikely to look at photos. Just because you have photos of marijuana plants does not mean that you grew them.

FLOWERING

CULL FAN LEAVES?

Jorge,

I have 6 plants in a little closet so I have to dwarf them. Should I, or should I not, cull the fan leaves? I have heard yes and no. The buds are fine, but the upper ones seem to be thinner and sparser. All seems to be well after 10 weeks. They were taken from cuttings. ANY info would be appreciated.

Thanks,
EDGE in Canada

Dear EDGE,

NO! NO! NO! Do not remove any leaves. Leaves are where plants make food to sustain growth. Ripping off leaves is slow-assisted suicide. Remove leaves only when they are infected with insects or too damaged to be useful. Some growers remove leaves several days before harvest to prepare for harvest.

To make plants grow shorter, initiate flowering sooner. Turn the lights to 12 hours dark, 12 hours light when plants are 4 to 6 inches tall. Most varieties grow up to 12 inches taller when finished flowering.

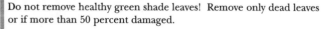

Super Size Secret:

Do not remove healthy green shade leaves! Remove only dead leaves or if more than 50 percent damaged.

TURN OFF THE LIGHTS!

Dear Jorge,

I'm growing 'White Widow.' Everything is going OK and healthy. I heard a rumor that the plant takes about 8 weeks to finish, and if you turn off the lights for 2 weeks it will put every bit of THC in the buds. Is this true? If it is, can you do it with other strains?

Everything Hydro

Dear Hydro,

Total bullshit! Keep the plants strong and healthy their entire life and they will produce the most THC. To date a 12-hour light, 12-hour dark regimen is best for flowering.

36 Hours of Total Darkness?

Hey Jorge,

MAAAANY thanks for your A1 advice. Much appreciated. You are the Guru!!!! I've been farming for about five years in Vancouver, Canada (eh....), and want to give a few "nuggets" back to the cause. When "flipping" from 18 to 12 hours, leave the plants in TOTAL DARKNESS for the first 36 hours. It will make them 25 percent taller because they "reach" for the light, and roots "reach down" deeper.

Take care,
Jackson, Vancouver, Canada

Dear Jackson,

Thanks for the kind words. I checked with several growers about "flipping" the light off for 36 hours before flowering. Their composite answer: Budding is a few days sooner and harvest is also a few days sooner, but the harvest is diminished proportionally. It does make them stretch and grow taller, and it might make the roots grow more.

Larry from THC-BC (Tel. 1-604-685-4769) told me of an experiment conducted by a Vancouver grower. The grower grew four different crops under diverse light regimens. In the first room he set the light to go on for 12 hours and off for 12 hours. In the second room, the light was on for 10 hours and off for 12. The light was on in the third room for 8 hours and off for 12. The fourth room had 8-hour days with 12-hour nights. The room with 8-hour days produced a fraction more every thirty days than the 12/12 room. The test was done only once, consequently, a "fraction more" was not verified twice.

The biggest problem with the short days was that the light would come on at odd hours, which made maintenance times confusing for the grower. For example, if the day/night schedule is based on 20-hour days (8 day + 12 night), the light comes on 4 hours earlier every 24 hours. The maintenance schedule has to be in tune with the days.

Let's go back to basics. If you are harvesting 0.5 grams per watt per month of flowering, start experimenting with different light regimens to see if you get a heavier harvest.

Jorge's Super Size Secret:

Electricity and lumens-per-watt are usually the limiting factor indoors. Grow as many grams per watt of light as possible to get the most from your garden.

BIGGER BETTER BUDS

Q Dear Jorge,

What can I do to make my buds bigger? Any old tricks or things you have used to increase the size of your buds?

J. Mann, Lodi, CA

A Dear J.,

The best thing you can do to grow the biggest, densest buds possible is to start with good genetics. Check seed catalogs for descriptions and offerings. Next, make sure the plants get everything needed to grow the biggest best buds possible. A strong healthy plant will produce the biggest best buds. Think of an Olympic athlete that eats well, gets plenty of rest and trains properly. They get peak performance by having all of their facilities working to their maximum capability. A trainer would never mutilate or starve this athlete to improve performance. The same holds true with plants.

Rapid unrestrained growth every minute the plant is alive is the secret to a heavy harvest. Most plants grow to maturity in less than 90 days. If plant growth is impaired by a lack of nutrients, light, carbon dioxide, etc., growth slows. It could take a week or longer to recover from the slowdown. This lost week means lost weight.

Many growers swear by a heavy feeding schedule, giving plants progressively more phosphorus, potassium and calcium and low nitrogen levels until about a week before harvest. North American growers tend to "flush" out excess fertilizer salts by irrigating with plain water. Other growers use products, such as Final Flush, a few days before harvest so flowering plants can be fertilized almost until the time of harvest. This regimen will increase bud weight and size. Leafy green growth will be at a minimum. A hydroponic growing system is necessary to control the nutrient availability and uptake with precision.

A high-sugar content in foliage and flowers means plants are taking up and assimilating the highest levels of nutrients. The easiest way to increase the sugar content during flowering is to add some sort of sugar to the irrigation water. Sugars that are not taken in via roots are easy to flush out weekly. Dilute molasses, fructose, Karo syrup, etc. into irrigation water and watch buds swell. A good friend in southern Spain has been experimenting with adding sugar to the irrigation water. He adds from one to three tablespoons of sugar per liter of water. He has found that buds weigh about 20 percent more than when sugar is not added.

TRICKY FLOWERING

Q Jorge,

I have an indoor plant that I tricked into flowering by placing it in a dark room for two weeks. The plant is 4 months old, six feet tall and has been flowering for more than 2 months. I have never grown a plant long enough for it to bud. I use a combination of regular florescent and also grow florescent bulbs. I give it 16 hours of light a day and water once a week with 10-60-10 liquid fertilizer. The plant is growing thick green foliage and still producing flowers on the new growth. Will this plant ever produce buds?

Thanks,

J. Wannabud, Ontario, CA

A Dear J.,

That plant is lucky to be alive! First rule, higher plants need light to grow and flower. Without intense light from the proper spectrum, they are unable to produce chlorophyll and grow, let alone flourish. Thanks for bringing it out of the closet.

Grow shorter plants or bend this one so the lamps can be as close as possible to foliage. The plant does not receive enough light from the fluorescents. Light fades fast, especially artificial light. Fluorescent light must be close (2-12 inches) to foliage to do any good at all. A 6-foot-tall plant does not get enough light to form descent buds. I am guessing the amount of light this plant receives is barely enough to keep it alive. I'm amazed that it is actually putting on new growth.

Cannabis is triggered to flower when nights become long and days short in autumn. The widely agreed upon schedule is 12 hours of darkness and 12 hours of light to induce flowering. Your out-of-the-closet plant is being tricked into believing it is still summertime. The 8 hours of darkness and 16 hours of light send the plants the signal to continue to produce green leafy growth. When you put it in the closet for two weeks, it received 24 hours of uninterrupted darkness. When you moved it out of the closet, flowering had been induced, but giving it 16 hours of light threw it back into vegetative growth.

BUDS TASTE LIKE FERTILIZER

Hey Jorge,

We love to smoke bud so much that we always run out before the next crop. Then we have to pick some of the buds before they are completely mature to stay loaded. Every time I pick buds they taste like the fertilizer smells. Somebody told me that I should rinse the crop out with plain water and not use fertilizer for the last two weeks to flush out the fertilizer. Is this true? Wouldn't it slow the plants down and make them produce less?

Jimbo

Dear Jimbo,

Growing a plant for a short time and pumping it up with lots of fertilizer for 6 to 10 weeks during flowering really packs the fertilizer in the plant tissue, soil or hydroponic substrate. Do this quick test to check me out and find out how much fertilizer is built up already. Take a dissolved solids or electrical conductivity parts-per-million (PPM) reading of the water coming out of your tap and record it. Flush one of your plants with one gallon of this plain tap water and catch the water that drains out the bottom of the pot. Now measure the PPM of the drained out water. Chances are very good the PPM reading of the drain water will be higher than the original water. The reason? fertilizer buildup in the soil or hydroponic substrate.

This experiment proves that fertilizer builds up in the soil or hydroponic substrate. Fertilizer also builds up in plant tissue, but is more difficult and time-consuming to flush out.

When fertilizer salts (nutrients), regardless of origin, chemical or organic, are at high levels in harvested buds, they can be tasted when consumed. Burn a bud packed with fertilizer and it crackles and tastes like the fertilizer smells. It's that simple.

To alleviate fertilizer taste, growers rinse their plants with plain water from one to two weeks before harvest to rinse out fertilizer from soil and to let plants use all the nutrients in the plant. This practice does retard development somewhat and may lower harvest a bit. How much is subject to debate. I have seen no evidence that the difference is notable. I believe buds smoke so much better that a very small decrease (one percent or less) is well worth the difference in taste.

There are products, Clearing Solution and Royal Flush, that draw all the nutrients out of plant material in a couple of days. If you are using these products, you can continue to fertilize until the last two or three days before harvest.

MALE FLOWERING

GOOD BOYS, BAD BOYS

Dear Jorge,

HIGH TIMES articles and Clarke's book *Marijuana Botany* have approached the subject of enhanced THC breeding, but none seem to provide a sound scientific answer to male selection without using a gas chromatograph. How do I find the "best" male plant to increase THC content in hybrids? Is smoking the male the only way or is there an inexpensive chemical test?

Farmer Jed Bodine, Houston, TX

Dear Jed,

Science is expensive and dangerous when it comes to male potency. Analysis with a gas chromatograph yields the exact content of THC for sure, but I don't know of any in the US that are legally available to the public. In the Netherlands, tests cost about $50.

Male plants are the most important and difficult to select for breeding. The first test is to rub the stem. The more pungent and resinous the odor, the more THC-potent the plant in general. The second test is to smoke the mature male tops. Only problem is, once mature, males shed pollen, possibly pollinating females. A painstaking option is to clone males before flowering them. Smoke the flowered males and you still have a pollen-producing clone. Male plants are highly prized and difficult to find. Major breeders have selected from thousands of males to find the right one.

SEEDY GIRLS

Dear Jorge,
Is pollen able to live on plastic or Mylar fastened to the wall? My last three crops have been seeded. Do I have to empty out the room to eliminate this problem?

Thanx. Cecilia, Mississippi

Dear Cecilia,

Pollen will stay viable for quite a while if it is not baked by the sun or moistened by water. The nightly TV news in Southern Spain has hemp pollen warnings about the pollen that drifts northward from Morocco! But, my guess is that you have unstable plants that produce occasional hermaphrodite plants. Hermaphrodite plants have both female and male flowers on the same plant. A few rogue male flowers can easily pollinate an entire indoor crop of females.

MALE PODS

Jorge

I have a friend who is trying to grow about 12 plants under a 430-watt HPS light in a 5 x 5-foot area. They are on a 24-hour light cycle. The plants are about 3 weeks old now and for some odd reason, two of them are showing male pods. They have always been under 24 hours of light. Can you tell me why they are showing their sex under constant light? Thank you.

Sincerely,

A Bud Smokin Friend

Dear Bud Smokin Friend,

Cannabis breeding exploded in the mid-1980s when the original Seed Bank opened in the Netherlands. Since then, more than a hundred seed companies have opened their doors to disseminate a menagerie of genetic material (seeds) throughout the world. The genes from plants from northern climates that flower very, very early as well as ruderalis varieties that are prompted to flower in relation to their chronological age have been bred into the old standard varieties. Some of these plants flower after a few weeks of growth, regardless of the photoperiod (ratio of day to night length).

Watch them closely and examine daily, to ensure they are really male plants. Once they develop pollen sacks, remove them from the garden to prevent spontaneous fertilization and ensure a sinsemilla harvest.

This drawing shows female seed bracts' development and aging.

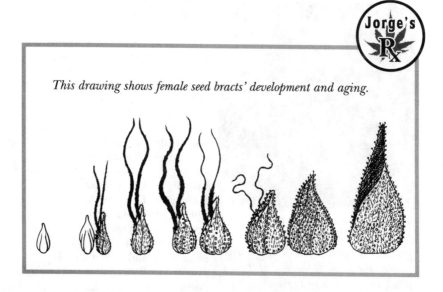

POLLINATION

High Jorge,

Say there are a small number of 'Chronic' plants growing indoors under a 1000w metal halide. When would be the best time to pollinate? How long does the pollen have to stay on the bud before the bud becomes pollinated? How long will it take for the unused pollen to die?

Thanks

Reproman, Philadelphia, PA

Dear Reproman,

'Chronic' is a great choice to grow. It is a good producer and relatively easy to grow. If the seeds are high quality, breeding is probably unnecessary and will probably result in lower overall quality in the next crop.

You can pollinate as soon as the white hair-like pistils are prominent. Pistils grow from the seed bract located on the buds. Clusters of pistil-containing seed bracts form buds. About 4 or five weeks after turning the lights to an even 12/12 (day/night) photoperiod, there should be plenty of pistils showing and peak pollination is most opportune. Pollination happens very quickly, within a few seconds. However, exposing pistils to pollen overnight ensures complete pollination of the target pistils. Very little pollen goes a long way. Unless you want the entire crop to bear seeds, you need to pollinate only one branch to have an ample supply of seeds. Containing the pollen will be your biggest obstacle. As soon as you see pollen sacks start to form on a male plant, isolate him from the females, preferably as far away as possible. The male will produce pollen even if he receives less (fluorescent) light. Within a few days to a week pollen will start to fall from the pollen sacks that have formed. Collect the pollen by placing a plastic bag over single branches or the entire plant and shake. Pollen will collect in the bag. Remove a female plant from the grow room. Carefully take this bag and gently place it over a branch covered with female pistils. Secure the bag at the bottom with string or wire tie. Shake the branch to ensure pollination. Leave the bag on the isolated plant overnight. Carefully remove the bag the following day and mist the pollinated plant with plain water, and return it to the grow room. Water will kill any viable pollen.

This beautiful sinsemilla bud is packed with white hair-like female pistils. One grain of male pollen will fertilize the ovule at the base of the pistil, causing a seed to form.

HARVEST
PEAK POTENCY

Dear Jorge,

From the commencement of flowering, what is the average time until the buds are at optimal potency? Are there any physical changes to help nail the proper time to harvest? I have been told new flowers have clear to milky-white resin but turn rusty red within 2 or 3 weeks. If you remove flowers to vaporize, will the pruning produce more flowers?

Thanks for fighting The Good Fight.

Uncle Eye, Somewhere In The Known Universe

Dear Uncle Eye,

Once the light regimen is changed to an even 12/12 day/night, flowering is initiated and visible signs appear about 2 weeks afterward. Stem tips elongate, internodal space increases and two tiny white hair-like pistils appear at branch nodes. Resin starts to accumulate heavily about the fifth week of flowering. Resin glands will first appear clear or translucent. Once resin glands reach peak potency, they change to an amber color as they start senescence, slow degrading. All of the resin glands do not reach the same point at the same time. Once at least 50 percent of the glands start turning amber, is usually the peak time to harvest. With a 30X hand-held microscope you can have a close-up look and actually distinguish the different resin glands. The most potent marijuana is packed with capitate-stalked trichomes (resin glands). These trichomes appear as a short post or stalk with a small ball or bulb on the top. At its peak, capitate-stalked trichomes are translucent and the ball is round and intact. As senescence sets in, trichomes turn amber and the bulb on top of the stalk deforms, getting smaller.

Picking little buds early to puff even if there is no smoke will retard flowering. If you pick too many little buds, yield could diminish too. If you must have early smoke, you are best off to grow a few sacrificial plants.

WHEN TO HARVEST?

Dear Jorge,

When do I harvest my buds. I know that I need to wait for the flowers to fill out and for the pistils to turn red or brown. The pistils are red, but they're just poking out the end of the pods because the pods themselves aren't opening. Should I pick or wait awhile?

Danny, Internet

Dear Danny,

Waiting is the most difficult part of growing!!! Unpollinated female marijuana (sinsemilla) is ready to harvest after the buds have filled out and the (normally) white hairs (pistils) have begun to turn red or brown. Indoors, they turn color from 6 to 12 weeks after the light has been turned to 12 hours. Most plants, except for those containing a lot of sativa genes – 'Haze', 'Skunk #1', etc., will be ready within 8 to 9 weeks.

In general the buds are ready to harvest when about half of the pistils have changed color. At this point of diminishing returns, the THC is decomposing faster than it is being manufactured. Harvest a bud or two, dry it in the microwave oven on the defrost cycle for 5 to 10 minutes and give it a taste. If it doesn't get you quite high enough, wait a few days and try it again.

HARVEST SOON

Dear Jorge,

I have a friend who is a month away from harvest. He wants to add the flavor blueberry. How can he do that? He does not have enough room to dry entire plants, so plans to harvest each bud as it is ready, then put them in a dehydrator. Will the lower buds get bigger and will the dehydrator harm the nugs?

Thank you very much
The Happy Home Grower, Cyberspace

Dear Happy,

GroTek from BC, Canada manufactures Final Flush. It is well distributed in North America. This product flushes away fertilizer salts and raises the fructose (sugar) level in plant tissue. It is available in strawberry and piña colada flavors. While only a subtle fruit flavor is imparted, the saltless plant tissue tastes much better when smoked.

Add buds to the dehydrator as picked. Turn the dehydrator on the lowest possible setting so buds dry slowly. Some growers use dehydrators without turning on the fan or heat. When dried over a few days, buds usually smoke smooth. Check bud moisture by bending stems. When they snap, they are dry.

Jorge's **Warning:**
Light, heat and friction from fondling hands all degrade resin and THC content. Keep buds in a cool dark place and keep fondling to a minimum!

GETTING BENT

Jorge,

I am a first time grower who unfortunately purchased your Indoor Bible too late. I kept a 18/6 vegetative light schedule for 90 days. I changed to 12/12 photoperiod 30 days ago. Now I have a 6-foot monster plant that is about 3 inches from my 400w lamp. I cannot move the light any higher. The lower portion of the plant appears to have normal bud growth. Will being too close to the light harm the main bud on top? Can I do anything to prevent/protect it? Does flowering for an extended period affect quality? None of the pistils are turning brown yet, however, there are signs that lower buds are ripping. If plant continues it will touch the bulb.

Thanks,

The Hobbyist, Internet

Dear Hobbyist,

Sounds like you grew a pure sativa from a bag of Mexican, Columbian or Hawaiian weed. Pure sativas are famous for growing tall with ample space between branches when subjected to low light levels. Bend the plant around so as to lower the profile. You may want to set up a "screen of green" (SCROG) about four feet from the top of the container and train buds and branches so they are on the same horizontal plain. This way the light will shine equally on most of the plant. The problem with such a tall plant is that most of the light has dissipated by the time it is three or four feet away from the bulb. If the central bud, or any foliage, gets too close to your plant, it could easily burn it. Keep foliage at least a foot away from any lamp, further if it is a 1000w bulb. Burned buds stop growing and do not produce.

It's difficult to tell how long it will take for your plant to finish flowering. Pure sativas can take 12 weeks or longer to finish. Often some buds will become ripe before others and should be harvested as they become ripe. Check for ripeness with the naked eye by allowing at least half of the pistils to turn brown. If you have a 30X microscope peak ripeness is when about half of the resin glands have turned amber and started to biodegrade.

DRYING
TEMPERATURE AND DRY TIME

Jorge,

What is the ideal temperature and length of time to dry your buds? My crop came out way too dry. I just bought the video *Sea of Green* and it says to dry buds for 3 weeks. I did it for 5 to 7 days and mine were too dry and harsh smoking.

Wolf, Tacoma, WA

Dear Wolf,

Ideal time to dry buds depends on temperature, humidity and density of the buds. Drying converts 75 percent or more of the freshly dried bud into water vapor. About 25 percent of the bud weight remains.

If bud is dried too fast, moisture is evacuated unevenly and it smokes harshly. If the drying room is too hot, volatile oils (resin) will dissipate. The rule of thumb to tell when a bud is dry enough to smoke is to bend the stem over. When the stem snaps, it is dry enough to smoke. Another test is to roll it into a joint and see if it burns.

Keep the drying room 60 to 70 degrees and the humidity less than 80 percent to dry buds in about 5 days. The trick is to keep testing the bud to make sure it burns. For super complete information on drying and curing check out the *Marijuana Grower's Guide* by Mel Frank.

Air, light and moisture biodegrade dry marijuana. Vacuum sealing dry marijuana will help keep it fresh for a year or longer. Molds and fungi must have air to grow. Excluding air keeps them at bay.

STORING WEED

Jorge,

I lived in Europe last year until September and smoked some of the finest 'White Widow' in the world. I stored two kilos (4.4 pounds) for when I return back from the US this year. It's stored in a bag inside a closet. Will it be good smoke when I get back a year later or will it make me sick?

Thanks very much for the help.

Mr. C. from Chicago, IL

Dear Mr. C,

Good news! If you extracted all the air from an impermeable plastic storage bag before hermetically sealing it, your pot will remain pristine for many months when stored in a cool dry closet. Bad news! If you kept the keys in a paper bag exposed to air and sunlight, deterioration is iminent and you will return to half the high you left. If heavily infected with fungus, the stored stuff could make you sick, especially if you are prone to respiratory ailments. But cooking is always an option.

CURE MY WEED

Jorge,

Growing is not an option where I live and suppliers are few and far between. The weed I buy is usually wet and improperly cured. What is the best way to cure improperly cured weed? Am I doing more harm then good by putting it under a light to dry? Do I damage the buds if I put it in a humidor for a day or two?

Thanks ,
Wyld Bill, Internet

Dear Wyld Bill,

Wet weed is the curse of an underground dope economy! Weigh it when you buy it. Set it out on the counter for a day or two and weigh it again. You will find that you paid dearly for grams of water! When dry, stems should snap rather than bend, and it should burn easily. Light and heat cause resin glands to biodegrade more rapidly. Keep the weed out of bright light. Re-humidifying in a cigar humidor is not detrimental, but unnecessary if properly dried.

HASH

HASH OIL

Dear Jorge,

I have saved about 7 pounds of good leaf from past crops. I want to make hash oil from them but can't find an ISO II isomorizer machine anywhere. I can't even locate anyone who has even heard of one. Where can I get a hold of an isomorizer?

Tropical Budsman, Miami

Dear Budsman,

There are lots of ways to make hash oil without a spacey looking ISO II. Check out the book *Cannabis Alchemy*, Ronin Press, $14.95.

Hash oil is made by liberating the THC locked in the plant with the help of a solvent. The oil is then smeared on rolling papers, mixed with marijuana or smoked in a pipe.

You may also want to make hashish out of the leaves. The procedure is simple and inexpensive. The result from low-quality leaves would be a low-quality hash that is probably a pretty fair smoke.

To make simple hash, you rub leaves or tops over a framed silk screen. The silk screens come in several sizes. A 100-mesh screen is a good starting point.

The THC-rich resin crystals are small and fall through the screen at a much faster rate than the green leafy matter. The Pollinator from Amsterdam is a drum shaped screen that spins. Resin is separated from leaf as the drum spins. For more information on the Pollinator, call the inventor and owner of the Hemp Hotel, Mila, in Amsterdam at 011-31-20-625-4425. Pollinators are very popular throughout Europe. You could also check out *Hashish!*, Redeye Press, $29.95 for more serious recipes.

The harder you rub the leaves the more green matter falls. The softer the rub, the more THC-rich crystal falls from the leaf through the screen. The powder is then collected below the screen and pressed into hashish.

To press, wrap powder in a cellophane wrapper and apply pressure. Often growers walk around with a piece of hash in their shoe. The constant body weight presses the hash into a solid piece.

With seven pounds of leaf, you could make one or two ounces of decent hash.

HASH BOOK

Jorge,

I was wondering if you could refer me to some books on how to make homemade hash and the cheapest way and best way to grow indoors.

Sincerely,

Brian from Buffalo

Dear Brian,

Hashish! by Rob Clarke, $29.95, is the classic book on Hash and hash-making. A must-have for all hash aficionados. *Pot for Pennies*, HIGH TIMES publisher, and *Marijuana Indoors: Five Easy Gardens*, by Jorge Cervantes are the two best books to buy for beginners. Both books are available from the HIGH TIMES bookstore.

You can see resin glands in this beautiful block of creamy Moroccan hash. Resin glands fall through a screen when dry plants are shaken. The residual resin glands and other debris is collected and pressed into hashish.

BREEDING
MULTIPLE CHROMOSOMES

 Jorge,

I was wondering about the effects of colchicine treatments to marijuana plants. What are the effects on the output of the plants? Are there any health risks due to using colchicine? How much research has been done? How available is the product? I understand that it doubles the genes in the plant making it have polyploid sets of chromosomes. How will this affect the next generation of plants?

J. Spade, Lansing, MI

Dear Spade,

Colchicine, sold by laboratory suppliers, is a very poisonous alkaloid and definitely not a cool chemical to put on seeds or plants that will be consumed. Plant breeders introduce it to plant tissue by soaking seeds or spraying a dilution on foliage. It is used to increase plant chromosomes in horticulture and to treat gout in medicine.

Cannabis has sets of chromosomes that occur in pairs within cells in normal diploid plants. These chromosomes transmit hereditary characteristics such as potency, leaf shape, sex, etc. Polyploid plants have more than one set of chromosomes inside of each plant cell. Polyploids have chromosomes in groups or sets of three or four. Tetraploid plants have cells with four chromosomes per group. Some breeders believed that since polyploid and tetraploid plants had more chromosomes, they would yield more cannabinoids, especially THC. Experiments to prove that polyploids are more potent are nonconclusive. Polyploids and tetraploid plants are abnormal and their extra chromosomes appear to have little or no impact on THC content or production.

Polyploids and tetraploids do not occur naturally and must be induced with treatments of colchicine. Once treated, there is no guarantee that plants will become or remain polyploid or tetraploid.

I have asked numerous breeders about their experience using colchicine. All of them said they do not use it and do not like it because it is poisonous and does not make plants more potent. For a complete discussion and specific directions on using colchicine, for what it's worth, see *Marijuana Botany* by Robert Connell Clarke, available at HIGH TIMES bookstore.

Many breeders have experimented with polyploid and tetraploid plants believing they would produce more potent plants. Polyploids can be induced with applications of colchicine. However, colchicine is poisonous and polyploid plants are not more THC-potent nor do they have any other redeeming qualities.

HOPS AND CANNABIS

Dear Jorge,

Can hops, the plant used to make beer, actually be used to disguise growing or is this a cruel hoax? Can any plant serve this same purpose? Also, I have 4-5 years to study before I grow. I was wondering if there any plants that resemble marijuana that would be good to practice with and any good books you can recommend?

Thanks,

Mike H.

Dear Mike,

It's a misguided hoax. Hop foliage grafted to cannabis rootstock will not produce THC. Grow annual vegetables and flowers. Grow all types of plants, regardless of the type. The more you know about all plants, the better grower you become. Visit with gardeners and hang out at the nursery. Check out the HIGH TIMES bookstore. *Marijuana Grower's Guide, Pot for Pennies* and *Indoor Marijuana Horticulture* are excellent books!

YIELD
FINE TUNING

Jorge,

I'm a professional grower and I'm not maximizing the total yield. I'm growing on a 4 x 16-foot hydroponics table with 8, 1000w HP sodium lights. I'm averaging about 0.8 lbs. a light. I'm sure I should be getting around 1.5 - 2 lbs. per light. I do all the normal things like topping and whatnot. I also use very highly recommended strains such as 'Shishkaberry' and 'Blueberry.' If you had my situation, what process would you take exactly?

Should I "Sea of Green" the table? I have about 200 plants on the table and each plant sits in a 4-inch rockwool cube. I'm thinking of packing the table next run with 400 plants.

Canadian Cropper

Dear Cropper,

I love your question, and it is one that should concern all growers. Grams per watt per 60 days, also expressed as ounces per 1000w lamp per 8-week flowering cycle are the true measure of production. Lose perspective on these figures and you are no longer a commercial grower, you are a wannabe.

You are producing 12.8 ounces per 1000w lamp every 8 weeks or 0.363 grams per watt (GPW) per 60 days. That's about one third of the harvest you should be achieving for the amount of light you are using.

You have too much light for your space. A 4 x 16-foot table = 64 square feet. You need only four, 1000w HIDs to provide the absolute maximum of light. Cut your light in half and you will double GPW to 0.726 per 60 days. Set up another 4 x 16-foot table illuminated by the extra four lamps double your harvest.

Now you can start to fine-tune your grow operation. Right now you have three plants per square foot of growing space. The varieties you are growing produce big fat buds and I don't know how there would be space to fit twice as many plants. My guess is that the foliage of each plant covers the other plant. You may want to experiment with lowering the nitrogen content of the nutrient solution a week or so before inducing flowering. Also try inducing flowering when plants are 4 to 6 inches tall. Change the nutrient solution every 4 or 5 days so nutrients are always balanced. Maintain the pH at 5.6-5.8 and follow fertilizer dosage guidelines.

After fine-tuning the garden you should easily achieve one gram per watt per 60 days. However, with the information at hand, I can't make more detailed recommendations.

SEA OF GREEN YIELD?

I am thinking of using the Sea of Green method, but before I use it I was wondering if you could tell me what kind of yield I would get every 2 weeks. I read that you can get a quarter pound (4 ounces) per square foot of growing space from a good plant.

Thanks

Da Mad Hatta

Dear Hatta,

The Sea of Green is one of the most intensive and productive growing methods possible. The growing technique got its name because the plants look like a "Sea of Green" on the growing table.

By your calculations a 10 x 10-foot growing area would produce 50 pounds per month. 10 x 10 = 100 square feet x 4 (ounces) = 400 ounces per 2 weeks x 2 = 800 ounces per month. 800 / 16 = 50 pounds a month from this garden. I don't think so!

Measuring yield per plant is as difficult as measuring yield per square foot. The only way to measure indoor yield consistently is by grams per watt of light per 30 days. I have seen lots of grow Sea of Green rooms. Seldom do I see

Three of the resin glands seen on leaves and buds are from left to right: bublous glandular trichome, capitate-sissile glandular trichome and the capitate-stalked glandular trichome. The capitate-stalked glands contain the lions share of THC.

one that produces more than 0.5 grams per watt of light. This means that a 10 x 10-foot room with the maximum of light – 2400 watts (four 600w HP sodiums) – yields 1200 grams of dried smokeable bud. 1200 grams / 454 = 2.64 pounds. If everything goes just right you should be able to harvest 0.5 grams per watt of light in the flowering room.

LIGHT CYCLES AND PRODUCTION

Dear Jorge,

I have four ladies about 2 feet tall and almost 3 months old. At two months I reduced their light to 12/12 hours day/night to induce flowering under a single 430w HPS. After three weeks, I increased the lighting cycle to 18 on, 6 off. Will the increased light cycle (after inducing flowering) revert the ladies back to a vegetative state? Do I need to keep them on 12/12 to get some buds going? I've been topping them to keep the size down, but they only have little hairs on them and they continue to produce more vegetation.

Scooby Dew, Encino, CA

Dear Scooby Dew,

They must have 12 hours of total darkness for at least six weeks to produce smokeable buds. Most varieties mature in 6 – 10 weeks of a 12/12 cycle. Changing the cycle back to 18-hour days made plants revert to vegetative growth, and switching them back made them flower again. Bouncing the photoperiod around caused excessive foliage to grow on buds. It also prolonged flowering. Pinching buds back to nab some wannabe nugs diffuses floral hormones, further delaying flowering. I'm willing to wager these plants are a bit beat back and sickly from so much fond care. Check carefully for spider mites and eggs on leaf undersides. Once plants start flowering under a 12/12 light cycle, keep them in it until they finish flowering and don't pinch them back.

Technical Stuff:

The metal halide lamps produce light by passing or arcing electricity through vaporized argon gas, mercury, thorium iodide, sodium iodide and scandium iodide within the quartz arc tube (1). At the end of the arc tube is a heat reflecting coating (2) to control temperature during operation. Spring supports in the neck (4) and dome (3) of the outer bulb or envelope (5) mount the arc tube frame (9) in place. The bimetal-shorting switch (6) closes during lamp operation, preventing voltage drop between the main electrode (7) and the starting electrode (7). Most bulbs are equipped with a resistor (10) that keeps the bulb from shattering under temperature stress. The outer bulb functions as a protective jacket, contains the arc tube and starting mechanism, keeping them in a constant environment as well as absorbing ultraviolet radiation. Protective goggles that filter out ultraviolet rays are a good idea if you spend much time in the grow room or if you are prone to staring at the HID!

Initial vaporization takes place in the gap between the main electrode (7) and the starting electrode (8), when a high starting voltage is applied. When there is enough ionization, electricity will arc between the main electrodes (7). As the lamp warms up, the metal iodide additives begin to enter the arc stream. After they are in their proper concentrations in the arc tube, the character-istic bright white light is emitted. This process takes about 3 - 5 minutes

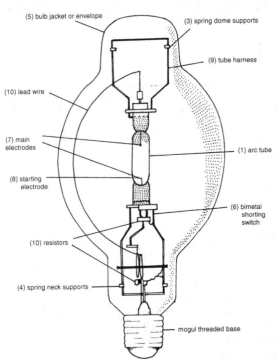

(5) bulb jacket or envelope
(3) spring dome supports
(9) tube harness
(10) lead wire
(7) main electrodes
(1) arc tube
(8) starting electrode
(6) bimetal shorting switch
(10) resistors
(4) spring neck supports
mogul threaded base

Diagram of a metal halide lamp shows each compo-nent.

POTENCY
TESTING FOR THC POTENCY

Dear Jorge,

I hear a lot about the percentage of THC in different varieties of herb. How do you test the percentage of THC? Can I buy a THC kit? I use herb for medical reasons, and I would like to know the amount of THC before I get my prescription.

Thanks,
Paul, CO

Dear Paul,

The test for THC is done with a gas chromatograph. Each test costs about $50. Each sample or new batch of cannabis would have to be tested to ensure accuracy. But, finding a laboratory with a gas chromatograph and an operator that is willing to do the test is very difficult. THC content fluctuates from one variety to another. Stress, harvest timing and aftercare also contribute to THC levels in relation to dry weight.

What you can do is find a reliable supplier that grows the same variety all the time and experiment with dosage. If it does not compromise your security or that of your supplier, you could visit the garden and learn a bit more about the growing process. Ask the grower to harvest the crop at the same time so the potency remains consistent. Drying should also be consistent, and avoid fondling buds, which knocks off and bruises THC-laden resin glands.

You can also check out the International Association for Cannabis as Medicine web site: www.cannabis-med.org for more pertinent medical information.

TIME AND POTENCY

Dear Jorge,

I smoke marijuana occasionally. Around 6 months ago I bought a nice gram of Maui and I still have it rolled in joints. Will the THC content degrade over time or will I get just as high as if it was first harvested?

P. H. R., Cyberspace

Jorge's Rx
Super Size Secret:
Check out the intensity "Light and Distance" chart to see what will happen if the lamps are one foot closer to plants.

Dear P. H. R.,

One gram in six months, your self-control is outrageous! You must be one of those guys that roll pinners! The best way to conserve potency in pot is to keep buds intact. Breaking up the bud fractures and bruises THC-rich resin glands, which speeds decomposition. But the way to preserve potency of the rolled joints is to store them in a dark airtight container in the refrigerator or freezer. The absence of new air, darkness and cooler temperature will slow decomposition to a crawl. For extra security, add a small packet of silicone crystals to absorb excess moisture and prevent mold. Then on the other hand, smoking one each morning would not let potency degrade anymore!

INCREASING POTENCY

Jorge,

I have lots of stems and leaves left over from my outdoor harvest. Is there anyway I can use them to make a THC extract? Does it increase the potency of the herb?

Mike, Louis, MO

Dear Mike,

Place leaves on a tray in the freezer overnight. The cold temperature will freeze foliage and resin glands. Once frozen, the glands and foliage become brittle and are much easier to separate. The glands tend to snap off in larger pieces and suffer less deterioration. Next, set the freshly frozen leaves on a coarse sieve, such as a coarse window screen with openings of 2-5 millimeters. Force the leaves through the screen with your hand and collect the sieved pot powder in a bowl. Now you are ready to separate the green from the resin. Place the pot powder on a tightly stretched nylon (or similar material, such as an artists silkscreen) sieve with a pore size of 135-150 microns. Use a business card or a playing card to gently brush the pot powder back and forth over the sieve. (Do not use a credit card or drivers license that you put back in your wallet! Customs officials love to pluck these items from you and check them for cannabis residue when crossing borders.) The concentrated resin glands below include the majority of the THC-rich resin in the leaves. You can smoke the resin solo by placing it on a screen in a pipe. Watch out, it expands in your lungs a lot when smoked. Or you can sprinkle it on a lack-luster bud to enhance the high. If you collect enough of the resin, you can press it into a small ball of hashish before smoking. Many such devices are available today, even though they are sold for other uses. The first such device, the Resin Heaven, was invented and marketed by Pypes Palace, in Portland, Oregon, Tel. 1-503-289-9298.

Technical Stuff:

Check out the "*Light Measurement Handbook*" available free on the
Internet. The 64-page technical book answers endless light questions.
Download the book in a few minutes, photos and all: www.Intl-
Light.com/handbook/.

HIGH ON VAPOR

High Jorge,

I have been reading HIGH TIMES for a long time and I love
Jorge's Rx. Is the high from a vaporizer the same high as smoking a water
pipe? Is it healthier for your lungs?

Thanks,

Dave, Miami, FL

Dear Dave,

Yes, the high is the same because the same cannabinoids are
ingested. But, it could fool you. When you smoke a bong or take a toke on a
joint, you are used to feeling the smoke come into your body and the proof
that you are smoking is realized when you exhale smoke. You also see the bud
burning. When you do not see these physical reinforcements, it is difficult to
believe you are smoking.

You still get all the same benefits of the bud, but with the health risks greatly reduced. THC, the psychoactive ingredient in cannabis, volatilizes into the
air at a lower temperature than it takes to burn the noble weed. Burning anything, including marijuana releases toxins – benzene, tuoluene and naphtha-
lene – in the smoke that can cause cancer. Inhaling this smoke of carcinogens
can cause cancer. Vaporizing the THC before the green matter burns will also
greatly decrease the release of carbon monoxide, tars and hydrocarbons,
none of which are good for your lungs or body. For more information on an
inexpensive portable vaporizer, contact danbo@efn.org.

POTENCY AND PHOTOPERIOD

Dear Jorge,

Does turning off the lights completely or down to 6 hours of light and 18
hours of darkness the last week or two of flowering increase the potency of a
plant? If it does not increase potency does it help in anyway?

Nameless in Nebraska

Dear Nameless,

Turning the light off completely during the last week of flowering will make plants grow very slowly or not at all. Turning the light down to 6 hours and 18 hours of darkness during a 24-hour day will also slow growth.

Potency is a function of genetics not cultural practices. More resin can be produced on less foliage by stressing plants in several ways including withholding water and slowing fluid flow within the plant. However, even though these methods cause more resin to form on less foliage, there is a proportionate amount of weight loss and overall, less resin is produced.

You are best off to keep plants very healthy and flower them under a regimen of 12 hours of light and 12 hours of darkness to grow the biggest heaviest and most potent buds.

GRINDING BUD?

Hey Jorge,

Does grinding bud in a coffee grinder remove a lot of the THC? It seems to me that it would, but the bud is so much easier to roll.

Coffeemaster, Richmond, BC

Dear Coffeemaster,

Grinders are all the rage and work well. Breaking up bud to an even consistency makes it burn more evenly and completely. Coffee grinders break up bud in short order, as do the new hand grinders such as the "Sweet Leaf." THC biodegrades in the presence of light, air and heat. Breaking resin glands into tiny pieces exposes more surface area to light and air, which speeds decomposition. Any time you break up bud to roll in a joint or stuff in a bowl, regardless of method, scissors, grinder or fingers, it accelerates decomposition. The trick is to do it just before toking so the buds experience the least amount of decomposition. Don't forget to scrape out and smoke the sticky resin that is flung against the walls of the grinder!

Jorge's Rx Super Size Secret:

Start with good seeds and reap a good harvest.
Start with great seeds and reap a bumper crop!

SEEDS

END THE CONFUSION PLEASE!

Hello,

I was a judge this year at the Cannabis Cup and sat in on Soma's lecture. He said that a sure way to tell if you have good seeds is to drop them in a cup of water. The good ones sink and the bad ones float? I was a bit stoned so my memory isn't clear. Does any of this make sense to you?

G13judge, Weed California

Dear G13judge,

Sure does. Everybody is supposed to be stoned at the Cup! Soma, a master grower and breeder, gives good advice. His simple test is tried- and-true for most seeds. The good seeds are heavier than water and the lightweight punky ones are not.

GREEN MAN?

Is Green Man a fake?

Lewis, A., Cyberspace

Dear Lewis,

We have to believe in heroes like Green Man! His page was pulled from the server over a misunderstanding. His new site is http://www.seedbankupdate.com. Green Man rates seed companies based upon e-mail he receives about the companies. He has been compiling information for several years. It is one of the best sites to find information from consumers about seed companies. Everybody should hit the site it is superb!

FEMINIZED SEED

Jorge,

I was growing 'Skunk's #1' and tried using the feminizing technique from your book. One turned out to be male and the other a hermaphrodite. When I harvested the hermie, the buds were half-male and half-female, and all of them got pollinated. Are the seeds from the hermie more prone to be females?

Thanks,
Doc, Cyberspace

Dear Doc,

Feminizing the seed starts with pollination. Dutch Passion owner, Henk, has developed a pollination technique for making feminized seed that utilizes hermaphrodites that are predominately female but have just a few, very few, male flowers. Pollen from such flowers is collected and used to pollinate receptive female pistils on a different plant. These are the basics of the procedure and as with anything, lots of experience including much trial and error will net the most consistent results. It took Henk several years and lots of tries to perfect this technique.

The information you read in *Indoor Marijuana Horticulture* (the Bible) discussed how environmental factors, not pollination techniques, affect plant sex. Female plants are more prevalent when:

The seed bed is rich in nitrogen
The temperature is low
The humidity is high
The root zone moisture is high
The light spectrum is more blue than red
The seedlings receive 14 hours of daylight
The seedlings suffer no stress

BEST SEEDS

Dear Jorge,

Out of all the seed companies that you have encountered, which is the best and the cheapest as far as quality seeds are concerned? I'm a 50-something-year-old man, and back in my day, you could get all the seeds you wanted just for the asking.

Thank you for your time.

Gary, near Milwaukee, WI

Dear Gary,

Telling you which seed company offers the best cheapest quality seeds is like asking which religion is best. The question is impossible for me to answer. What I can do is give you some background so that you can make an informed decision. Every year in the March edition of HIGH TIMES I write a seed company article that lists the top seed companies in the world. I suggest that you pick up a copy of this edition and read the seed article. You should also hit Green Man's site, http://www.seedbankupdate.com. He rates seed companies based on customer reports. It is subjective but honest and as accurate as possible.

Cannabis Clue:

Maintain the growing medium temperature between 75 - 80 degrees
F. day and night to root cuttings fast.

Back in your day, seeds were free because they were unstable and of ques-
tionable quality. During the last 20 years serious cannabis breeders have cross-
bred and stabilized many distinct varieties. Breeding is a lot of work, time
consuming, expensive and growing marijuana is illegal. This is why the seeds
are expensive.

MACHO SEEDS

Dear Jorge,

HELP! This is my third attempt to grow indoors. The first two times, 90%
of my plants turned male. I will be growing in a 2 x 4 x 7-foot room with 270
watts of high-pressure sodium light. I ordered the 'Dutch Treat' variety of
seeds from Iron Seed Bank. These seeds grow into short plants that bloom
quickly. I need to know how to store seeds for long periods of time. I also
need to know how I can seed out a couple of plants, so I will have plenty of
seeds for future use. I also need to know what light cycle to start off with.
When do I start flowering? I also need to know how to keep the root system
smaller, to keep it from getting root bound in the container. Will this make a
plant male-out?

J. B. Southwest Arkansas

Dear J.B.,

Plant stress is why the plants are turning into males. Under ideal conditions, seeds from reputable companies grow into female plants more than 70
percent of the time. Store the seeds in a cool, dry dark place in an air-tight
container. They should last about 3 years. However, the germination rate will
decline over time.

I do not suggest that you make your own seeds. The seed you buy is known
as F1. The seed is made by crossing two true-bred plants. The plants will have
hybrid vigor and grow about 25 percent bigger than non-hybrid seeds. You
would be making F2 seeds. Seeds are formed from a cross of two non-true
bred plants. These seeds are not guaranteed to grow into strong healthy
plants like the parents. They could easily loose potency and be weaker overall.
It is much better to find a female plant you like and grow clones of that plant.
This way the integrity of the plant is retained. If you want to pollinate a
branch or two of a plant, you must first collect pollen from a male plant.
Once you know you have a strong potent male plant – a real find for any
breeder – isolate the plant from the garden and let it produce pollen. Once

pollen is produced, collect it in a plastic bag. Put this plastic bag over one or two flowering branches of the plant you want to pollinate. Secure the bag on the branch with a wire tie. Let the bag stay on the branch overnight and remove it the next day. Do the pollination in a room separate from the garden to protect other plants from accidental pollination. Once pollinated, return the plant to the garden. Seeds should be ready when the garden has finished flowering. Let the seeds dry for a month or two before planting.

Start plants with 18 hours of light and 6 hours of darkness. Induce flowering when plants are 6 inches to one foot tall with a 12-hour day/night photoperiod. The root system should not be a concern if you are growing in at least 3-gallon pots. Plants will be harvested before plants become root bound.

A SINGLE PLANT

Dear Jorge,

I am thinking about growing a three to five foot plant, either from DJ Short or Paradise Seeds, in a small to medium sized closet. What is the best kind of light to grow just one plant? How far above the plant should the light be? Do I need a fan in the closet to circulate the air?

Mark, Nowhere in the USA

Dear Mark,

You might want to double your luck and grow two or three plants. Odds are that half of the seeds will turn out to be male, which are much less potent than females. If you have problems with diseases, pests, nutrients, etc., harvest could be diminished substantially. Plants could even die leaving you with no dope and starting over.

Until recently, I have been an exclusive fan of metal halide and HP sodium lamps. I have been looking into different lamps for small indoor gardens. Initial experiments indicate that you can use a 65w compact fluorescent floodlight that generates 6,800 lumens to grow and flower two or three small plants. They produce more than 100 lumens per watt, that's on a par with a 400w metal halide! The lamp has to be placed close to the canopy of the garden, about 6 inches away, to be most effective and the plant cannot grow taller than 2, possibly 3 feet for light to penetrate foliage. I suggest that you bend plants to keep the plant no taller than 2 feet. Compact flood fluorescent lamps are available in discount and building supply stores for about $30.

Jorge's **Super Size Secret:**

Keep the temperature of the rooting medium at 78 - 80 degrees F. and ambient air temperature 6 - 8 degrees cooler than the rooting medium, day and night. Root growth increases dramatically.

"CHOAD"

Hello Jorge,

My friend told me the sticky and yucky resin that sticks on the "walls" of my pipe was hash that's good to smoke. I think it is smokable but not good because it contains all of what you're happy not to smoke. Am I right?

Mr. Master, Internet

Mr. Master,

The tar-like residue, affectionately referred to as "choad", is what's left after burning bud. Cannabinoids volatize at a lower temperature than it takes to burn the bud. Essentially all of the THC and other cannabinoids have released their payload by the time temperature is hot enough to burn the marijuana. This is why you can smoke a vaporizer, volatizing cannabinoids and leave the buds enact. If your friend does not believe this simple explanation, let him choad down all the "hash" while you smoke the real thing.

SEX

SEX

Hi Jorge,

I'm a first time grower, and I was wondering if there was a way to tell a mama plant when it's still just a baby? I was told there was by a few people, is this true?

Cocotte, Internet USA

Dear Cocotte,

Yes. It is possible to distinguish a potential mama when she is young, however, it is not guaranteed.

Male and female plants generally have different growth characteristics. Male plants are generally taller with less foliage and thicker stems. Females are usually shorter, bushier and full of foliage.

About the 8th to 12th week of development male plants usually grow a single spur (stipule) at branch unions (nodes). This spur is often followed by a premature small almost indistinguishable pollen sack. Often, but not always, female plants develop two white hairs at branch unions. This development is sometimes accompanied by stem swelling. In both male and female plants

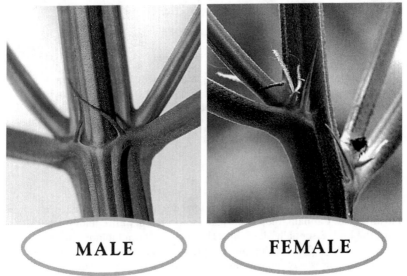

these developments occur a few inches below the top of the plant.

All female seed varieties are also available too. The Dutch seed company, Dutch Passion, produces all female seeds. They have been on the commercial market for at least three years and bloom out all female.

Cloning for sex is my favorite way to discern a mama. It takes about two weeks and is guaranteed. The plant should be at least two months old. Take two cuttings of all the plants you want to know their sex. Label each clone and corresponding parent plant. Give the cuttings 12 hours of uninterrupted darkness and 12 hour of light every 24 hours. Fluorescent light is the best. The cuttings will show their sex within two weeks. Remove the male clones and corresponding parents.

NOTE: Anytime plants are stressed by lack of water, too much water, light (hours of light per day/night) fluctuation, cold or hot temperatures, excessive humidity or dryness, etc., the chances of sex reversal increases dynamically. Growers' report that stressed plants tend to turn male.

BOYS AND GIRLS

Hello Jorge,

Recently, I found 3 plants growing in a little flowerbed in my backyard. They get plenty of sun and water. How do I tell if they are male or female plants? If they are male, will I still get budz? I mean I am willing to do what it takes to get these plants to grow to their fullest, but I need your help.

Thanx for your time,

Still Smokin'
Adrienne, Oklahoma City, OK

Dear Adrienne,

What luck! By this time of year, boys and girls should be easy to tell apart. Male plants contain much less THC than female plants, but they will get you high. Like females, the majority of the THC is contained in and near the flower tops, but male flower tops are much more lightweight than female buds. The pollen, however, will not get you high and should be avoided.

Remember to yank the males before they shed pollen on female flowers. Unpollinated female cannabis buds are "sinsemilla," Spanish for "without seeds." If male pollen pollinates female flowers, seeds develop. A female is pollinated when a grain of male pollen slides down the pair of white hair-like pistils that protrude from the seed bract. THC production essentially stops as soon as seeds start to form in female flowers. If you have seen imported seeded marijuana, you know that half of the bud weight is seed.

Fertilize plants regularly with a mild liquid mix. Change to a flowering fertilizer in mid to late August. Bend plants so they blend in with the rest of the garden profile and foliage. Theft is probably your biggest obstacle the month before harvest.

MISCELLANEOUS

SMOKIN' HONEYMOON

Jorge,

My fiancée and I are trying to find the perfect place for our honeymoon. Being everyday smokers, this is a burden. Do you have any suggestions on where we should go? Weed appreciate any thoughts you have.

Thanks!

Stoners in Love, Cyberspace

Dear Stoners in Love,

My picks in order of importance include: Amsterdam, Holland, Vancouver, B.C., Barcelona, Spain, and Jamaica for a smokin honeymoon. If you decide on Amsterdam, there are many inexpensive flights into the city. Stay at the Hemp Hotel, Fredricksplein 15, 1017 KX Amsterdam, Site: info@pollinator.nl or dial 011-31-20-625-4425 from the US or Canada to make reservations via telephone. Double occupancy about $55, which includes a hemp breakfast. You may have seen the hotel featured on *Lonely Planet's TV* travel focus on Amsterdam. Everybody speaks English. In Vancouver, BC, check out The Amsterdam Seed Co. Bed & Breakfast, Tel: 1-604-728-5617, Site: www.theamsterdam.com. The rates are $100 for a double and $130 for the master (honeymoon) suite. A smoke-friendly environment located 30 minutes from world-class snow skiing at Whistler/Blackcomb. In Barcelona, it's easiest to fly in and take the bus or taxi into the city. Go to the "Barrio Gotico," the old part of town, it's where everything is happening. There are numerous hotels in the area and you can always find a vacancy. Smoking is tolerated behind closed doors in most hotels and at night bars. Ask the bar-tender before firing up to be polite. Hash costs from $5 – 10 per gram and is available from street venders. Watch for good quality. Jamaica is another good hit. Check out Negril at the local travel office.

AMSTERDAM

Jorge,

My pot-loving girlfriend and I are going to the motherland, Amsterdam, but I don't know a thing about the city. Can you spare a minute or two and share some advice that would be helpful on a stoner's first trip to Amsterdam? What are some good places to stay that won't dig too deep into our meal and marijuana money? Good coffee shops to visit? Coffee shop etiquette and/or age-restrictions to shops?

We both love HIGH TIMES and take comfort in knowing that there are others like us who are offended by the hypocrisy of a government that allows the use of other state-altering drugs like alcohol and tobacco but comes up with reason to draw the line at marijuana.

Stoned and loving life,

Forma420, Cyberspace

Dear Forma420 and Friend,

You will have a wonderful time!!! Airfare is lower starting September 15, after the summer rush. Fly into Schipol airport and take the train into town. Arrive at the Central Train Station. Walk out the front door, go a couple of blocks down the street and take a left at the Dam Square. Turn left on Achterburgwalstraat. Look for the Cannabis College on the left. Tell Lorna, the director, that Jorge Cervantes sent you.

Pick up a copy of *Get Lost, The Cool Guide to Amsterdam*, and check out the sites www.hiptravelguide.com/amsterdam and www.hazetv.com for lots of up-to-date information. The sites are run by good friends with impeccable taste. Coffee shops were having a difficult time keeping up with demand this summer and occasionally sold moldy dope. Look at all purchases in the light to ensure quality. It will be difficult, but try to pace yourselves, you won't run out of dope!

MOVING TO CANADA

Dear Jorge,

I have heard that Canadian drug laws are more relaxed than in the U.S. I am considering moving there to cultivate. Could you tell me what the laws/penalties are for cultivation/possession/distribution are in Canada or tell me where to find it? I greatly appreciate it.

A Devoted Fan in the US

Dear Devoted Fan,

You are not the only one that is moving to Canada to cultivate, but beware! Immigrants are required to register with Immigration. US citizens can stay in Canada for 6 months, but must also register. Growers who cross the border and stay as illegal aliens, do not bring any incriminating evidence with them. They mail or ship it across the border. Best advice is to talk to several illegal alien growers and find out their details, cautions and recommendations.

The greater Vancouver, BC area and the Montreal area are the most popular grow locals. This summer the Vancouver police estimated there were 20,000 grow operations (up from 10,000 two summers ago) in the Vancouver area (population 3.5 million). That's one grow op for every 175 people. The police had "taken down" only 600 grow ops in the last year, or 3 percent of the estimated grow shows. If these numbers are correct, chances of getting caught are slim. Here is the good news, only a fraction of the busts went to court! The exact letter of the law is not as important as how the laws are applied. For exact legal details contact a lawyer where you plan to live. My best guess is, that your worst-case scenario is deportation and "persona non grata" status. Enforcement in the Montreal area is a quarter that of Vancouver. Law enforcement presents little problem in Montreal and Quebec Province, but the bikers are a formidable force. Two rival groups, the Hells Angels and the Rock Machine, not only battle for turf, they control numerous grow rooms, growers and much of the marijuana trade. Growers in Montreal tell me they are much more afraid of the bikers than the cops. Other parts of Canada, especially Alberta, are not pot friendly. The further you get from the big cities, the less pot friendly. If you decide to go north, spend a few weeks looking around and talking to growers. Be cool and don't flash a lot of cash.

MOLDY ROACHES

Dear Jorge,

When I finish joints I empty the roaches into a film container. Soon I have enough to roll a few more, smoke some bowls or whatever. But, some moisture got in the container, and the weed has a very thin film of mold around it. Is it OK to smoke or should I chuck it out?

Mr. Mildew, Southern Alabama

Dear Mr. Mildew,

Moldy dope is a drag. Fungi that deteriorate stored bud include *Aspergillus, Penicillium, Rhizopus* and *Mucor* species. All "storage molds" flourish in limited moisture low oxygen environments, such as that of a closed storage jar. Individuals with asthma and suppressed immune system disorders, such as AIDS, should never smoke moldy roaches or marijuana, especially if it is contaminated with *Aspergillus* species. When smoked in a joint or pipe, *Aspergillus* and *Mucor* species exit the mouthpiece of the smoking device before the smoke. Burning the weed will not destroy the fungus. Medical marijuana patients must take extra precautions. One test with *Aspergillus* contaminated bud smoked through a water-filtered bong reduced the fungal spores by only 15 percent. Vaporizers heat bud to 355-375 degrees F, (180-190 degrees C) which vaporizes the active ingredients, THC and other cannabinoids, without burning the bud. You could also bake the roaches or moldy bud in the oven at 150 degrees F (65.5 degrees C) for five minutes before smoking. The 150-degree F temperature kills *Aspergillus* spores, but does not kill *Aspergillus* antigens, which could still affect tokers with suppressed immune systems. About 10 cases or involving *Aspergillus* were reported in San Francisco in 2000, according to the Centers for Disease Control and Prevention

Many times mold on "dry" dope is undetectable by the naked eye. Upon close inspection with a 30X magnifying glass, you can often see signs of mold. Once the fungi have progressed, it is easy to see and can appear as white to gray clumps or tufts that may release a cloud of spores when disturbed. *Mucor* and *Rhizopus* spores are usually grayish-black, *Penicillium* spores pale bluish-green and *Aspergillus* dark greenish-black.

Fungi also deteriorate marijuana causing it to loose weight and potency. A black light (UV, 365 nm spectrum) such as a Wood's lamp that is made specifically for such detection causes contaminated dope to glow a bright greenish-gold color.

For a complete discussion on post-harvest fungi, including detailed drawings, see *Hemp Diseases and Pests*, by J.M. McPartland, R.C. Clarke and D.P. Watson, ISBN: 0-85199-454-7.

Avoid all of the above problems by drying dope properly. Dry it in a cool well-aerated dark locale. Most fungi that attack drying marijuana require ultraviolet (UV) light to produce spores, which reproduce more fungi. Storage fungi will not live on dry cannabis when the moisture content is 15 percent or less. A good rule of thumb for testing to see if the cannabis is dry enough to store is to bend a dry stem. If the stem snaps rather than folds over, the cannabis probably contains less than 15 percent moisture.

LIDS?

Jorge,

I'm just about to 4:20, but before I do, I have a question. I was watching one of my favorite movies, Cheech and Chong's *Up in Smoke*, and I noticed the excessive use of the word "lid." I concluded that the word is used to express an amount of marijuana, but was wondering how much?

Always faithful smoker,
S. J. Sahara

Dear S. J.,

There are two-fingered lids, three-fingered and four-fingered lids. Marijuana used to be sold by the lid, the amount of pot that could fit in a small container. Plastic Baggies were very big in the 60s when the term "lid" became popular. Marijuana dealers would bag up and sell the equivalent in volume of dope – one finger is equivalent to 7 grams. So a three-finger lid would be about 21 grams. A four-finger lid, 28 grams or an ounce. Oh, to go back to the old days!

SKEWERING STEMS

Jorge,

I heard that if you damage a plant's stalk before harvest it will raise the THC in the plant. Is this true or not?

W. M., San Antonio, TX

Dear W. M.,

Yes, scarring and mutilating a plant's stem can increase the THC content of the plant. The theory is that more resin is produced to ward off pests and disease. The THC produced is not more potent. I do not advise this practice because any increase in THC that might occur is more than off-set by a smaller harvest. Beating up plants by skewering the stem and removing tissue also provides a path for fungus, disease and insects to attack. Concentrate on growing strong healthy plants from seeds that provide the genetics for a high content of potent THC.

COOKING CANNABIS

Jorge,

I have heard that frying weed in butter before putting it in brownies will result in a running-around-goofily-while-giggling-and-babbling-like-an-idiot high, while just chucking it into the batter will result in a collapsed-on-the-couch-for-the-duration kind of high. Any confirmation/denial?

Tototoo, Internet

Dear Tototoo,

If you want to fry, sauté the weed at a low temperature. Stovetop cooking at higher temperatures will burn the butter and possibly disperse the cannabinoids (THC is the most desirable cannabinoid) into the air. Once the cannabinoids are combined in butter, an oil base, it is ready to use for baking. Combining cannabis with butter, cooking oil or alcohol, liberates and disperses the cannabinoids so they are easy for the body to assimilate. They are totally ingested by the body and reach their fullest potential. That's why they have more effect. The actual high depends on the potency of the original cannabis used to cook the weed.

Not liberating the cannabinoids in an oil/alcohol, will result in poor absorption. Often the cannabinoids will pass through the body with little or no absorption. I know people that have eaten dried buds with no affect at all.

Be careful when eating brownies or "space cake." It takes about an hour for the high to hit full force and it is easy to forget and keep eating when you have the munchies. A couple of Canadian friends recently baked up a bunch of brownies containing about 14 grams (0.5 ounces) of 'Blueberry' bud. They chowed down and went on a nature walk. When they were about a mile and a half from home the high hit them full force. It took them three hours to crawl home on their hands and knees. It started to rain on the way back and by the time they got home they were drenched and covered with mud.

Jorge's Rx

If you've got a great recipe that you want to share with the world, submit it to our website, MarijuaunaGrowing.com as a new story.

COFFEE SHOPS IN VANCOUVER, BC?

Dear Jorge,

I'm planning on taking a trip to Vancouver, B.C. and I want to hit the legal pot cafes that I've heard so much about. I went to the HIGH TIMES website looking for a directory of cafes around the world. No luck. You guys (and gals) have always been kind to me in the past. Please help again, I would hate to be unprepared for Canada.

Sincerely,
Cristobal M., West Coast

Dear Cristobal,

Although marijuana use is tolerated and smokers seldom arrested in Vancouver, cannabis is still illegal. Vancouver has no "coffee shops" that sell marijuana. The closest thing you will find are bars and cafes where people smoke marijuana and independent dealers may meet clients there to make transactions. Most of which are located downtown on lower Hastings Street. The best known is Blunt Brothers, located at 317, West Hastings, Tel: 1-604-682-5868.

Make the return trip hassle free and don't bring any weed, seeds or marijuana-related items back to the US. If you smoke in your car, vacuum it thoroughly, wash the inside windows and dashboard before crossing the border.

JANUARY
OUTDOORS

Make plans for outdoor crop. Order seed catalogs and surf the net for new varieties and deals on old reliable strains. Plan/make trips to acquire seeds.

Start outdoor seeds if you live in a warm climate.

Buy the Western Garden Book. It is packed with climate information.

Look for good localized garden information in the newspaper, magazines and at the County Extension Service.

Go to straight garden shows to get fired up for spring planting.

Go to local nurseries and pick nursery peoples brains about climate, soil, fertilizers, etc.

Check saved seeds to ensure they not suffering moisture damage.

Stay stoned and make New Years grow resolutions! Get mentally prepared for spring planting.

INDOORS

Check the www.hightimes.com website for Cannabis Cup winners. Order your favorite seed.

Cold outdoor weather can cause indoor temperatures to plummet unexpectedly. Humidity often climbs in cold weather. Growing mediums often stay too wet when humidity is high, causing water use to decrease and EC top climb. Keep humidity near 50 percent (day) and 60 percent (night).

Cold grow room floors slow water uptake. Roots turn brown and mushy and rot when over-watered.

Move pots up off floors. Substrate and nutrient solution below 65 degrees F can slow nutrient absorption.

Warm intake air if cold temperatures cause problems.

Flush plants with water or a mild nutrient solution once a month. Fertigate with full-strength nutrient solution after flushing.

Mask smell with sprays or neutralize odors with an ozone generator.

Inspect & spray for spider mites that cannot live in freezing outdoors.

Harvest enough for New Year parties. Start the New Year stoned.

Take clones to start a new crop as needed.

If tripping during the holidays, fill reservoirs and water plants before leaving. Do not leave gardens alone for more than 3 days!

FEBRUARY

OUTDOORS

Plan a ski trip to Whistler, BC (1-877-933-7888 or www.whistlergolf-tours.com) and make a seed stop in Vancouver.

Order seed catalogs by mail or hit seed sites on the net. Check out www.seedbankupdate.com for a current list of great seed companies.

Cultivate grow holes and add amendments.

Plant seedlings indoors in warm climates. Move into heated greenhouse. Short days and long nights in spring will induce flowering if plants are 6 to 8 weeks old. Harvest buds before longer days in April.

Go to local garden shows and read local garden information. Buy a *Farmer's Almanac*.

Examine saved seeds for mold. Properly stored seeds should be kept in a cool dry place in a dark container.

INDOORS

Cold outdoor temperatures often affect the indoor climate, making humidity soar and temperatures drop. Water use will decrease and nutrient concentration will increase. Inspect roots carefully for damage. Adjust temperature and humidity accordingly.

Cold intake air causes lower grow room temperatures. Preheat incoming air if necessary.

Scrutinize humidity both day and night and keep at or below 60 percent to avoid problems.

Use an ozone generator to control fragrances.

Check runoff nutrient solution. The strength, measured in EC or PPM, should be lower than input nutrient solution. If the EC/PPM is too high, deficiencies and excesses result. Leach excess fertilizer salts monthly from containers to avoid problems.

Take clones to be ready for the next crop.

Examine leaf undersides, stems and roots for pests and eggs. Spot spray with aerosol pyrethrum or Einstein neem oil.

Harvest ripe buds/plants. Refrain from harvesting early.

Replace harvested plants with clones in perpetual gardens. Clean up and move in clones.

MARCH

OUTDOORS

Spring has sprung in southern states, but freak cold snaps can kill plants. Bring plants in if temperatures dip below 50 degrees F.
Cultivate grow holes. Add organic elements to holes.
Plant gardens in warm climates now.
Start hardening-off plants for remote gorilla gardens.
Grow young plants in deep containers so a deep root system develops.
Cultivate a spring crop. Clones set out in warm climates the first or second week in March will receive about 12 hours of light.
Look for new grow areas. You can never have enough places to plant!
Transplant hardened-off seedlings and clones. Set a Wall-O-Water over them. The water-filled tepee holds tender plants down to minus 20 degrees F.!
Add a packet of silicon to jars and sealed bags of dry bud to ensure they stay dry and well preserved.

INDOORS

Outdoor day/night temperature change can make humidity climb quickly at night. Measure and control nighttime humidity and avoid associated problems.
Keep humidity below 60 percent. Pay special attention to the humidity just after the lights go out. This is when it climbs the fastest and causes the most problems.
Measure pH and EC of the fertilizer nutrient solution daily and plot on graph to find inconsistencies.
Plants may start using more water and a little less fertilizer now. Keep a vigilant eye on growing medium moisture.
Crank up the ozone generator to control pungent bud odors.
Flush plants monthly to avoid nutrient buildup problems.
Take clones and be ready for the next crop.
Examine leaf undersides, stems and roots for spider mites, eggs and other pests. Spot spray as needed.
Harvest ripe buds/plants. Wait till buds are ready!
Grow clones to plant outdoors. Prepare older mother plants to transplant outdoors.

April

Outdoors

Hit the site www.usna.usda.gov/Hardzone/ushzmap.html, to learn the last average day of frost in your area. It is relatively safe to plant outdoors one month after this date.

Move plants outside during the day and indoors for cool nights.

Grow seedlings under a Wall-O-Water if temperatures dip at night.

Heat greenhouse substrate with electric cables or mats. Move in young plants to harden-off.

After first frost, transplant hardened off seedlings and clones. Set a Wall-O-Water (www.shop.store.yahoo.com/seedsofchange/wallowater) over them.

Order seeds!

Sprout seeds to move outdoors. Check local garden columns or with the local nursery to learn the last average day of frost in your climate. Plant seeds 6-8 weeks before this date.

Peruse local newspapers and garden shows for sales.

Change packets of silicon in seed storage jars to ensure preservation. Stored seed's greatest enemies are moisture and heat.

Indoors

Warm outdoor temperatures speed fertilizer uptake by plants.

Top off hydroponic reservoirs with water/nutrient solution daily.

Measure EC and back off on fertilizer dosage to compensate for increased water use.

Evaluate pH and EC of the fertilizer water or hydroponic nutrient solution at the same time every day. Plot results on graph paper. Inconsistencies will help diagnose plant nutrient deficiencies.

Do not let humidity climb above 60 percent both day and night.

Inspect plants carefully for insect and spider mite damage.

Control odors with an ozone generator. Warmer weather increases pungent fragrances.

Flush pots every two to four weeks and avoid many problems.

Make clones that are well rooted, robust and ready for next crop.

Start clones and harden-off to plant outdoors. Harden-off mother plants to move outdoors.

Harvest ripe buds/plants. Refrain from harvesting early!

Clean up grow room daily. Grow room should be as clean as a hospital kitchen for best results.

MAY

OUTDOORS

Direct seed in ground outdoors or start seedlings indoors.

Transplant well-rooted seedlings/clones when they are at least a month old.

Harden-off clones/seedlings before moving outdoors. Move plants indoors if temperatures dip below 55 degrees F.

Remove 1-4 sets of leaves and plant seedlings deep. The subterranean stem will soon sprout roots. Plant so 2-3 sets of leaves are above ground and the rest of the plant is below ground.

Apply snail/slug bait around plants. Apply granular Bt (Bacillus thuringiensis) to kill caterpillars. Cover with a chicken wire to protect from rabbits and deer.

Mulch older plants to conserve and attract water.

Fertilize with a high nitrogen mix. Use a soluble fertilizer if you are able to water plants weekly. Use a granular mix if unable to fertilize regularly.

Natural foliage dieback causes a tale-tell well-worn path to the patch. Take a new route to the patch each time to avoid detection.

INDOORS

Plants use more water and less fertilizer when outdoor temperatures climb. Top off hydroponic reservoirs daily. Check the (EC or PPM) strength of the solution daily.

Keep humidity below 60 percent both day and night to avoid disease problems. Growth slows above 75 degrees and essentially stops above 85 degrees F.

Examine foliage for disease, insect and spider mite damage.

Keep the ozone generator fired up. Fragrant plant odors are much more volatile when weather is warm.

Avoid problems by flushing containers and hydroponic gardens every two to four weeks.

Take clones for next crop. Grow clones for 2-3 weeks or until they have a strong healthy root system.

Harvest ripe resin dripping plants and prepare for the next crop.

Harden-off clones, seedlings and old mother plants to plant outdoors.

Clean grow room and keep it clean to avoid problems.

JUNE

OUTDOORS

Direct seed in ground. Seeds and seedlings need plenty of water. Small plants dry out quickly during hot weather.

Strip leaves from the bottom of the stem and plant deeply in the ground. Leave at least two sets of leaves on top of plants. Subterranean stem will sprout roots.

Add water absorbent polymer crystals to planting hole. Crystals retain water and lessen irrigation frequency.

Protect seedlings and clones from slugs, caterpillars, rabbits and deer.

Water needs increase substantially from June through the first week or two in September.

Mulch around plants heavily.

Fertilize with a complete mix containing more nitrogen than phosphorus and potassium. Apply a soluble fertilizer if able to water plants weekly. Apply a granular mix if unable to fertilize regularly.

Bend and tie plants down to avoid detection.

Shade pots exposed to direct sunlight to protect roots from cooking.

Much native foliage is dying back. Take a new route to the patch each visit to avoid betraying trail.

Ask nursery people grow questions about tomatoes and apply the information to marijuana.

INDOORS

Increase water to fertilizer ratio to offset escalating water use.

Replace nutrient solution and clean reservoir weekly.

Adjust humidity to 60 percent or less both day and night to avoid problems.

Inspect each plant for disease, insect and spider mite damage. Insects and spider mites are much worse when weather warms. Spot spray as needed.

Hot weather intensifies odors and it is important to keep the ozone generator running to avoid problems with neighbors or police.

Flush growing medium every two to four weeks.

Take clones two or three weeks before harvesting crop.

Harvest resin-squirting buds. Move in the next crop of clones.

Clean room and avoid problems!

JULY

OUTDOORS

Water recently planted seeds and clones religiously.

Record your rainfall for the month.

Water plants as needed. Give one inch per week for strong growth.

Fertilize with a complete mix containing more nitrogen than phosphorus or potassium.

Mulch!

Check foliage and roots for pest/disease damage. Spray as needed.

Set out slug and snail bait.

Check local nursery, newspaper or extension service for seasonal pest and fungus plagues.

Remove males as soon as you see them.

Visit garden only as needed. Brush along trails tends to grow slowly in July and August.

Always take different paths to the patch to diminish attention.

Vacationing kids, hikers and motorcyclists are outdoors to enjoy free time and good weather.

Bend and tie plants down to avoid detection.

Shade pots exposed to direct sunlight to protect roots from cooking.

Black out back yard and balcony crops every night to receive 12 hours of complete darkness. Harvest early buds in 8-10 weeks!

INDOORS

Humidity climbs exponentially for every degree temperature drops. Extra ventilation could be necessary at night too.

Plants can use twice as much water in hot weather.

Cool grow room by running lights at night.

Flush plants with plain water once or twice this month.

Increase ozone or other odor abatement.

Take clones to start a new crop as needed.

Halt CO_2 generator if it causes temperatures to climb too much.

Go on regular "search and destroy" missions for spider mites, whiteflies, thrips and aphids.

Cool nutrient solution in hydroponic systems to guard against wilts. If unable to cool, add anti disease/fungus solution.

Measure EC and pH of irrigation runoff water to check for nutrient buildup and acidic growing medium. Correct by flushing and raising pH of nutrient solution.

Harvest plants when ripe.

AUGUST

OUTDOORS

Water is critical. Visit all pot patches this month to water plants.

Fill a backpack with dry grass clippings and use for mulch.

Check with local nursery, newspaper or extension agent for seasonal plagues of insects or fungus. Control pests/diseases as needed.

Cover bait to exclude warm-blooded animals and moisture from lethal toxin. Scare munchie manic deer away with repellents.

Fertilize plants with bloom formula to stimulate flower growth. Cut back on high nitrogen formulas.

Remove male plants as soon as they appear.

Be wary of being watched when visiting plants by Rambo-wannabe cops that get paid to keep America free of "immoral gardeners".

Protect plants from heat by staking and shading with other plants so that the scene looks natural. Shaded plants use less water.

Shade potted plants from the glaring sun.

Always take a new path to your patch to avoid making a distinct trail.

INDOORS

Temperatures are hot this month and plants use more water.

Ventilate room all night if humidity is high.

Cool grow room by running lights at night.

Flush plants with plain water once or twice this month. Fertigate after flushing with nutrient solution.

Increase ozone or other odor abatement if crop is flowering.

Take clones to start a new crop as needed.

Suspend CO_2 generator use.

Inspect plants carefully for insects and eggs. Spray as needed.

Cool nutrient solution in hydroponic systems to guard against wilts. If unable to cool solution, add anti disease/fungus solution.

Top off reservoir once or twice daily. Clean and replace nutrient solution at least once a week.

Take clones 2-3 weeks before harvest.

Harvest beautiful buds when ripe.

Scour away salt stains and residue from pots and reservoirs before moving in next crop of clones.

SEPTEMBER

OUTDOORS

Make a rainy day plan to harvest plants early to beat possible bud mold.
Water and mulch plants regularly when blooming.
Check foliage and roots for insect and fungus damage and control.
Reset slug/snail bait. Check for and control pests.
Search out and destroy male plants.
Fertilize flowering females for the last time. Use an organic super bloom
    formula so taste is sweeter.
Watch out for hunters, many are anti marijuana.
Harvest early varieties before thieves do. Cut ripe budded branches from
    plants, wrap in paper or cloth, insert in backpack. Hang branches to
    dry in safe location.
**Harvest when calyxes in buds are swollen and at least half of the hair-like
    pistils protruding from calyxes should be brownish-amber. Use a 30X
    magnifying scope to see resin glands on bu**ds and leaves. Harvest when
    half of the capitate-stalked trichomes (resin glands with a round top)
    turn from translucent to amber in color. The bulbous head disfigures
    as it decomposes.
Shade pots from broiling sun.
Take different paths to your garden every trip.

INDOORS

Humidity climbs at night. Ventilate room all night if humidity is high.
Monitor moisture daily. Plants use much water when temperatures climb.
Fertilizer needs increase in hot weather, but not as fast as water needs.
    Give plants weaker fertilizer solution because they will be transpiring
    more water.
Cool grow room by running lights at night.
Flush plants with plain water once or twice this month. Fertigate after
    flushing with nutrient solution.
Increase ozone or other odor abatement if crop is flowering.
CO_2 generators create too much heat in warm weather. Stop using if hot.
Inspect plants carefully for pest insects and eggs. Control.
Check roots for fungus gnats and rot. Treat gnats with Gnatrol and wilts
    with Pythoff.
Use a sulfur evaporator against bud rot and physically remove bud mold.
Make clones 2-3 weeks before harvest.
Harvest!

OCTOBER

OUTDOORS

Be ready to harvest any time. Watch the weather and yank plants before a freeze or big rain even if it's a little premature.

Water regularly until 2-3 days before harvest.

Check for latent hermaphrodite male flowers on female buds. Harvest entire buds or plants that show hermaphrodites.

Do not fertilize.

Avoid game wardens, park rangers and hunters. Often deer hunters perch themselves in trees.

Harvest most varieties in most climates should be harvested in October. See September for more information.

Drying: Have a place ready to dry your bounty. Remember, drying buds really reek when drying. Cut branches or entire plant at the stem. Remove large leaves by hand. Hang branches or entire plants from drying lines in dark ventilated room.

Watch for thieves and harvest if you think crop is in danger.

Use different trails to the garden even during harvest.

Dig plants up, put them in a pot and bring indoors to re-bloom! Give them 18 or more hours of light daily for two months. Induce flowering with 12/12 day/night photoperiod.

INDOORS

Clip cuttings from outdoor flowering plants. Root your favorite outdoor plants indoors.

Temperatures cool this month. Turn on the CO_2 burner again.

Keep nighttime humidity below 60 percent.

Monitor and control moisture daily.

Fertilizer needs decrease as weather cools. Water needs may also decrease. Increase fertilizer dose slightly.

Flush plants with plain water once or twice this month.

Odors might remain pungent. Keep your nose to the wind!

Inspect for pests and root rot. Take control measures.

Take clones to start a new crop as needed.

Harvest!

Clean room thoroughly and move in the next crop of clones.

NOVEMBER

OUTDOORS

Buy airplane tickets and Judges Passes to the Cannabis Cup in Amsterdam ASAP. It's the last weekend of November. Hit the site www.hightimes.com for more information or go direct to www.420tours.com.

Most crops are out of the ground by November first. Late-to-mature sativa-dominant crops in warm might still be in the ground. Light intensity and hours of light per day are the main limiting factors to growth now. Avoid problems by harvesting this month.

Harvest, harvest, harvest! November weather is usually cold, wet and miserable in much of North America and Europe and if crops are not harvested by now they usually fall victim to mold or cold.

Plan for next year. Order seed catalogs, surf the Internet for information on outdoor growing and new seeds for next year.

Check www.hightimes.com for Cannabis Cup winners.

INDOORS

Turn on CO_2 burner to help warm grow room.

Humidity could drop in grow rooms if house is heated with wood or another dry heat.

Keep nighttime humidity below 60 percent.

Monitor soil moisture and irrigate daily.

Elevate pots a few inches above cold floors to warm substrate.

Fertilizer and water needs decrease with cool weather.

Flush excess nutrients from substrate.

Kill pungent odors with an ozone generator or carbon filter.

Inspect leaf undersides for pests. Control as needed.

Control fungus and (bud) mold. Sterilize tools and clean grow room with bleach.

Scour away salt stains and residue from pots and reservoirs before moving in next crop of clones.

Take clones 2-3 weeks before harvest.

Harvest!

DECEMBER

OUTDOORS

Harvest last outdoor plants in warmest climates this month.

Save seeds for next year. Store seeds in a cool dry place.

Add a packet of silicon to jars and sealed bags of dry bud and seeds to ensure they stay dry and well preserved.

Friends love joints, buds and candied buds for presents.

Recover from all the fun you had at the Cannabis Cup in Amsterdam.

Plan winter getaway! The weather in Amsterdam is usually clear and cold in the winter.

Plan next years crop. Order seed catalogs. Check Cannabis Cup winners and order favorites.

INDOORS

Temperatures outdoors are cold almost everywhere in North America. Turn on your CO_2 burner to fertilize air and heat the room.

Watch humidity both day and night. A maximum/minimum hygrometer records the extremes. Keep humidity near 50 percent during the day and don't let climb over 60 percent at night.

Monitor substrate moisture. Adjust irrigation schedule.

Elevate growing containers a few inches so cold floors do not cool pots below room temperature. Elevating pots in winter can increase and speed harvest.

Fertilizer absorption slows if the room cools. Watch plants closely for symptoms of nutrient deficiencies, especially nitrogen and calcium.

Flush pots with a mild nutrient solution monthly. If your plants show signs of toxic fertilizer buildup - burned leaves or abnormal growth and color, flush twice.

Odors from budding babes can add to the Christmas flavor of the home. Control with charcoal filter or an ozone generator.

Inspect leaf undersides and roots for rot and pests and control.

Harvest your biggest best buds for the holiday season!

Replace harvested plants with clones in perpetual gardens. Move clones into clean grow room after harvest.

INDEX

97, 99-104
McPartland John 102
Medical use 13-15, 17, 89, 102
Microwave 78
Mixing, fertilizers 36, 38, 41; growing medium 30-32, 36, 58
Moisture 34, 51, 54, 63-64, 78, 80, 89, 94, 102-103
Mold 60-62, 89, 100, 102
Mother plants 1, 5, 19, 28, 45, 60, 65-66, 100
Mylar 74
Narc 12, 16, 21
Netherlands 13, 38, 74-75
Noise 9
Nodes (internodes) 77, 97
Nursery 21-22, 31, 85
Nutrients, calcium (Ca) 2, 36-37, 61, 66, 71; iron (Fe) 45, 51, 95; magnesium (Mg) 36-38, 66; manganese (Mn) 45; nitrogen (N) 4, 38, 41, 46, 58, 61-62, 65, 71, 86, 94; phosphorus (P) 38, 41, 51, 61, 71; potassium (K) 38, 51, 65-66, 71, silicon 89; sulfur (S) 61-62; zinc (Zn) 84
Odor abatement 9, 49, 54-55, 58, 74; charcoal filter 54
Organic gardens 17, 32, 34, 45, 56-58; fertilizer 3, 31, 40, 43, 52-53, 73
Outdoor gardening 10, 15, 17-20, 22, 26, 30, 67-68, 89
Over-fertilization 40, 42
Oxygen 32, 44, 51, 102
Peat moss 67
Perlite 31-32, 34, 38, 52, 58, 64
Pests; aphids 59; fungus gnat 58; scale 59, 61; spider mites 20, 56, 61; whiteflies 57-59
Pollinator 82, 99
Pesticides; Bacillus thuringiensis (Bt) 58; miticide 56; neem 56; oil spray 57
pH 4, 32-33, 36-39, 42, 46, 50, 52, 61-62, 66, 86
pH testers 36
Pistils 3, 76-79, 94, 99
Planting 32, 35, 57, 63, 65-68, 96
Pollen and pollination 74-76, 94-95, 97, 99
Polyploid 84
Potency 19, 47, 74, 77, 84, 89, 91-92, 95, 102, 104
Propagation, see Clones and cloning, seeds
Propane 52
Pruning 49, 61, 67-68, 77
Psychoactivity 91
Rain 18, 37, 64, 104
Reflective hoods 22, 27, 29-30, 33, 60
Reservoirs 2, 44, 46, 51
Resin glands 77, 79, 81, 87, 89-90. 92
Respirator 30, 81

Ripeness 55, 79
Rooting hormones 1, 65, 67-68, 87
Roots 1, 19, 32-36, 44-47, 51, 58, 62-63, 66-67, 70-71, 85
Safety 30, 63
Salt (fertilizer) buildup 33, 35-38, 40-43, 71, 73, 78
Sea of Green 79, 85-86
Security 7-9, 11-12, 89
Seed bract 75-76, 99
Seedling 6, 21-22, 32, 63-65, 94
Seeds 1, 6, 8, 11, 13, 21-22, 28, 32, 40, 47-48, 50, 61, 63-65, 74-76, 84, 92-96, 98-99, 103, 105
Sex 65, 75, 84, 94, 97-98
Shade 33, 69
Sinsemilla 6, 75, 78, 99
Smoking 73, 80, 91-92, 97, 102, 104
Soap 57-58
Sodium 36-37, 46, 66
Soil, clay 36; organic 31, 45, 54; texture 31-32; potting soil 19, 26, 32, 40, 64
Soilless mix 30-32, 39, 45-47
Spider mites 20, 56, 61
Sprays and spraying 22, 46, 56-59, 61-62, 84
Sterilizing 32, 61
Stress 34, 65-67, 88-89, 92, 94-95, 98
Sunlight 26, 63, 81
Switzerland 12, 14
Tetraploid 84
THC 14, 39, 43, 69-70, 74, 78, 82, 84-85, 87, 89-92, 97, 99, 102-104
Thermometer 50
Thieves 15
Timers 17, 24, 55
Transpiration 52, 66
Transplanting 1, 19, 22, 35, 66-67
Traps 57, 59
Trichomes 29, 77, 87
Vaporizer 91-92
Varieties 28, 55, 89, 95
Vitamin B1 67
Watts-per-square-foot 30
Wind 18
Window 26-89
Wire ties 68, 76, 96
Yield 2, 5, 17, 23, 25, 28-30, 40, 45, 47, 49, 53, 67, 74, 77, 84-87

www.marijuanagrowing.com

Jorge's & Marijuana Growing

Jorge Cervantes is the author of *Indoor Marijuana Horticulture, The Indoor Bible*, and more than a dozen other grow books. Jorge's RX is a monthly column in *High Times* magazine, where he is considered the cannabis guru. Jorge Cervantes is internationally respected as one of the foremost researchers of marijuana growing.

This site contains a library of images and grow tips that put Jorge's wealth of knowledge and experience at your finger tips. Here you will find information about Jorge's books, videos, seminars, and personal appearances.

The Marijuana Photo Gallery is where you can view images from Jorge's lens or post your own.

The Marijuana Growing Forum is a good place to interact anonymously with other growers and trade tips and suggestions.

The Q&A section is where you can read questions and answers about growing marijuana from the guru himself. You can ask Jorge any cannabis growing question.

If you're serious about growing cannabis, and getting the best yields possible, read Jorge Cervantes books on marijuana growing.

THE SITE IS INTERACTIVE!
You can participate by adding your own reviews, comments, stories or event listings.

- Interview with Jorge Cervantes
- Indoor Marijuana Horticulture
- Can you tell me how other growers do it?
- How do I make clones step-by-step?
- How do I germinate seeds?
- How can I avoid diseases and pests?
- How do I set up a grow room step-by-step?
- What if my room gets too humid?
- What are the security issues when growing indoors?
- Is soil texture important?
- What is pH?
- What is fertilizer NPK?
- What should I consider when setting up a grow room?
- What is the difference between PPM, EC, TDS, DS and CF?
- What is THC, CBD and CBN?
- Harvesting Marijuana

MarijuanaGrowing.com offers information on these and other topics:

Breeding
Cloning
Grow Rooms
Hydroponics
Indoor Gardening
Legal Matters
Lighting
Nutrients
Other Topics
Outdoor Gardening
Pests
Seeds
Soil
Water

INDOOR MARIJUANA HORTICULTURE

by Jorge Cervantes
5.5 x 8.5", 420 pages, 200+ color photos, 200
b/w photos and illustrations, glossary, index.
Price $21.95 + postage